SHOSHANA LEPON

NO GREATER TREASURE

Stories of Extraordinary Women Drawn from the Talmud and Midrash

Targum / Feldheim

First published 1990

Phototypeset at Targum Press

Published by:
Targum Press Inc.
22700 W. Eleven Mile Rd.
Southfield, Mich. 48034

Distributed by:
Feldheim Publishers
200 Airport Executive Park
Spring Valley, N.Y. 10977

Distributed in Israel by:
Nof Books Ltd.
POB 23646
Jerusalem 91235

Printed in Israel

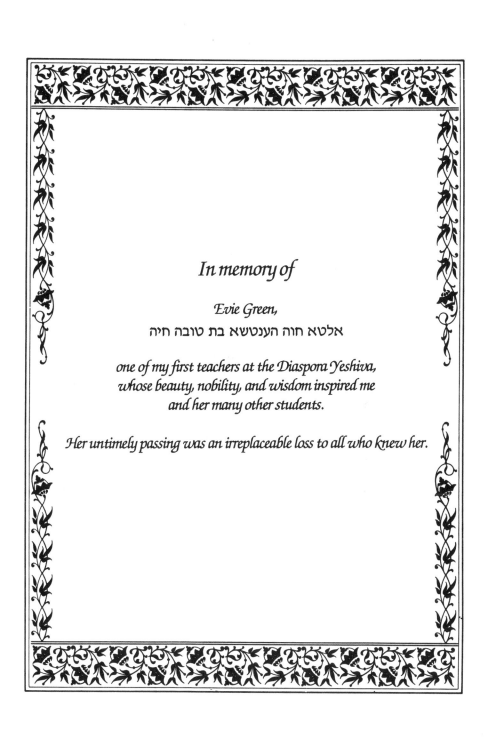

In memory of

Evie Green,
אלטא חוה הענטשא בת טובה חיה

one of my first teachers at the Diaspora Yeshiva,
whose beauty, nobility, and wisdom inspired me
and her many other students.

Her untimely passing was an irreplaceable loss to all who knew her.

This book is dedicated to:

- ❦ My mother, Mrs. Nina Loev, who embodies the optimism and idealism of the Jewish woman. She has never been afraid to alter her path in life, despite whatever hardships this entailed. By personal example, she has taught me a commitment to Torah values and a love for Eretz Yisrael.

- ❦ My mother-in-law, Mrs. Patricia Lepon, who embodies the grace and generosity of the Jewish woman. Her love and firm belief in us has been a constant source of strength.

- ❦ My teacher, Rebbetzin Mazal Goldstein, dean of the Diaspora Yeshiva Women's Seminary, who embodies the love of Torah and selfless dedication of the Jewish woman. The efforts she invests in both her family and an entire yeshiva have taught me an important lesson. In her classes she introduced us to *her* role models: the women of the Gemara and Bible.

Acknowledgments

I would like to thank Rabbi Dr. Mordechai Goldstein, Rosh Yeshiva of the Diaspora Yeshiva, for sharing his wisdom and encouraging me to write this book. In his weekly classes for women, he inspired us with a love of Torah. I am grateful that he took the time to give this manuscript serious attention.

In making numerous decisions with Targum Press, I always felt the staff had my best interests in mind. The quality of this book attests to their professionalism.

I am indebted to the following people for their insights: Rabbi Shimi Green, Rabbi Yissachar ben Avraham, and Rabbi Daniel Isaacs.

Yeshara Gold always found time to read over another story. She gave my manuscript the same care and concern she gives her own, and her comments were invaluable.

Finally, my husband advised me every step of the way. His enthusiasm for this book gave me the confidence to begin each new story.

Contents

A Note from the Publisher

The Aggadic portion of the Talmud has long been recognized as a treasurehouse of wisdom, brimming with lessons in faith, morality, and ethics. Although our world differs vastly from the world of Chazal, human nature remains the same. Only the setting has changed; man's potential for greatness has not.

Rav Yisrael Salanter, founder of the *mussar* movement, noted that reviewing the stories of Chazal is a powerful tool for self-improvement. If you wish to become a better person, he counseled, study the tales of the Aggadah. Moreover, use your imagination, your *koach hatziyur*, to incorporate these lessons into your life. (See *Michtav MeEliyahu*, vol. I, pp. 260, 315.)

This collection of stories was written with Rav Salanter's words in mind. Shoshana Lepon has skillfully used *koach hatziyur* to create a synthesis of many sources and commentaries, which are listed after each story. The result is a rich, colorful tapestry.

The words of Chazal can be interpreted in many ways, to teach many lessons. Obviously, a work of this kind cannot incorporate them all. Rather, in dramatizing a particular story, the author often followed one specific interpretation.

Though Mrs. Lepon has drawn her inspiration from the Tanach, Talmud, and Midrash, the dialogue and many of the details are her own invention. Following Rav Salanter's approach, she has used the power of imagination to create sixteen unforgettable tales of remarkable women.

אשת חיל מי ימצא....

A woman of valor,
who can find....

*T*he Sages said: "All flour [kemach] is
flour, but Kimchit's flour is finely sifted."
To Kimchit, the Sages applied the verse, "All the
honor of the king's daughter remains within;
she will be adorned with squares of gold."

(Vayikra Rabbah 20:11)

Squares of Gold

Kimchit straightened the scarf on her head before opening the door. "Shimon!" she cried when she saw her son, the high priest of the Jewish nation, standing before her. "What are you doing here? Don't you know that tomorrow night is Yom Kippur?"

"Could I possibly have forgotten, Mother?" said Shimon. "You see, I—"

"Come in, come in," the old woman hushed him. "You musn't stand out there like a peddler."

Shimon dutifully followed his mother into the house.

"I won't be able to perform the service this year," he sighed as he sank into a chair.

"What?" gasped Kimchit. "What are you saying? This is the most important service of the year. Everyone is depending on you!"

"I know, Mother," Shimon said wearily. "Last week I moved to special quarters to prepare myself for the service. I have hardly slept for days because every time I close my eyes, I see the Holy of Holies coming before me.... Then, I begin to tremble uncontrollably. To calm myself, I review the laws of the service one more time. I ask myself again and again, 'Have I sinned? What misdeed may prove my downfall, God forbid?'

"Then, this afternoon," he continued, "with Yom Kippur almost upon us, I received word that the king of one of the seventy nations wished to meet with me immediately!

"What could I do?" asked Shimon, as if his mother's silence were accusing him. "The sages said I could not insult him by refusing to come.

"During the course of the meeting, my garments became sullied, rendering me ritually impure. Now, I will have to wait a full week before reentering the Temple!"

"Oh, Shimon," said Kimchit softly. "You've been preparing for this day the entire year!"

"Yes, the entire year..." he nodded. "But you haven't forgotten who will replace me, have you, Mother? As of tomorrow, Yehudah will be your seventh son to serve as high priest."

"Of all days," whispered Kimchit to herself....

❧

"Of all days," Yehudah shuddered. He sat alone in the marble chamber with nothing but his own thoughts for company.

He had known all along that he might have to conduct a Yom Kippur service, yet now he felt himself totally unprepared. Indeed, how could one prepare for an experience that was without parallel in this world?

Just the thought of entering the Holy of Holies, the most private and sacred chamber of the Holy Temple in Jerusalem, was enough to make anyone tremble. Here, under God's unrelenting scrutiny, the merest trace of sin was fatal. For centuries, corrupt men had bought their way into the high priesthood. Of course, these charlatans could not survive the Yom Kippur service and a new high priest had to be anointed every year. Since the sons of Kimchit had been anointed the deaths had ceased, but who knew what lay ahead?

"How can I be sure that I'll fare better?" wondered Yehudah. "One should never trust himself until his very last day. Who knows what fault the Almighty may find in me?"

Yehudah's thoughts were interrupted by the arrival of several other priests. "Come with us," they instructed him. "It is time to be sworn in."

Yehudah hurriedly followed the old men down a hallway, struggling not to slip on the polished stone floor. Climbing a narrow stairway, they finally arrived at a chamber on the far side of the Temple.

Here the Avtinas family prepared the ritual incense according to a secret formula that had been passed down from father to son for generations. Even now, on the eve of the holy service, the secret would not be divulged, not even to the high priest. He would be taught the delicate art of taking the incense in his hands without spilling a single grain, and he would review the order of the service yet again, but the sacred mixture itself would remain a mystery....

❦

Kimchit sifted her flour once again. She had been in the kitchen since early morning, taking trays of golden squares out of the oven and mixing new batches of batter. Baskets and baskets of pastry were stacked up against the wall.

She lifted her bowl with shaky hands.

"I'm so nervous I can hardly do my baking," she told a friend who dropped by.

"It looks like you've made more than enough," her neighbor replied as she surveyed the room. "How many people are you planning to feed before the fast?"

"More than you can imagine," answered Kimchit.

Her friend looked at her in bewilderment.

"These cakes will be taken to cities of refuge later today," Kimchit explained.

The woman opened her eyes wide in a mixture of shock and fascination. "Whom do you know in the cities of refuge?"

"No one personally," said Kimchit, "but in a way I am tied to them all. These cities are havens for those who have accidentally killed others, but they can also turn into prisons. Even after the grieving relatives have abandoned their desire for revenge, these fugitives are forbidden to return home. They have one chance for freedom, only one opportunity to return to their homes. They are relesed," said Kimchit in a low voice, "upon the death of the high priest...."

"Don't even say that!" her neighbor hushed her.

"But that is the law," said Kimchit calmly as she bent to take another tray out of the oven.

"I still don't understand," pressed her friend. "What good can all these cakes do?"

Kimchit broke off a steaming piece of pastry and handed it to her guest.

"In two more days, on Yom Kippur, the high priest will enter the Holy of Holies to burn the incense. So many men have met their deaths in this holy place that they tie a rope around the high priest's waist in case he fails to emerge. This way, if his body must be removed, it can be pulled out from a distance, since no one else is permitted inside."

She paused and dusted her hands on her apron. "Have you ever stopped to think what this means to the people in the cities of refuge? Each Yom Kippur could spell their freedom. Each Yom Kippur could mark the end of their exile. Would you be surprised if some of these fugitives hope for the death of the high priest?

"That is why every year I bake baskets and baskets of sweet, golden cakes," Kimchit explained. "I send them to the people in all the cities of refuge, and I ask them to have mercy on me and pray for my son."

She packed away another basket and began to crack more eggs. She had been thinking of Shimon while baking the first few cakes. Now her thoughts turned to Yehudah, her youngest, the one who would always be her baby.

"May Hashem watch over him, and find him worthy," she sighed, beginning to sift more flour.

The neighbor tried to reassure her: "All your other sons have served as high priest in the past, and they did fine."

Yes, thought Kimchit, each of her sons had substituted for Shimon, and each had survived.

"What am I worried about?" she scolded herself. "Is Yehudah any less righteous than his brothers?"

Still, Kimchit could not repress a shiver. Tomorrow, her youngest son would stand before God, Who sees into man's heart. His life would be in peril, and with it the atonement of the entire nation.

"May the All-Merciful guard his coming and going," the women whispered. "May He guard us all...."

Yehudah rubbed his eyes and tried to focus on the words being read before him. It was forbidden for the high priest to fall asleep on the night of Yom Kippur, and assistants took turns keeping him awake.

Their voices droned on throughout the night. "'And the Lord said to Moses,'" one of the young priests recited, "'Take for yourself sweet spices: balsam and onycha and galbanum and pure frankincense.... And make it into incense...pure and holy. Grind it very fine, and place some of it before the ark...where I will meet with you...do not make it for yourselves according to its prescribed composition; it shall be sacred to God. Whoever makes it to enjoy its scent shall be cut off from his people.'"

"Grind it very fine...." "Not for yourselves...." "Sacred to G-d...." Yehudah's head began to reel. The young priests roused him by snapping their fingers before his face and making him stand barefoot on the cold, marble floor.

Yehudah heard a growing clamor outside the door. Although the sun had not yet risen, the Temple courtyard was already filling with people eager to escort him to his first Yom Kippur service.

Trumpets sounded and Yehudah looked up to see the same old men who were with him the day before standing in his doorway. "It is time," they said.

As they climbed the steep staircase, Yehudah beheld the crowds gathering below.

"Remember before Whom you are to stand," one priest solemnly reminded him.

"Remove all thoughts of pride from your heart," instructed another. "Only then can you serve as a conduit between the Almighty and the people."

"The nation is counting on you," whispered a third. "The moment you become aware of your own glory, not only will you die, but the expiation of Israel will be lost."

Yehudah's hot tears stung his cheeks. "Am I truly ready to stand before God?"

The trumpet blasts grew louder, the Levites sang, the timbrels chimed. The royal descendants of King David, the incense-makers, the Temple artisans, the seventy judges of the Sanhedrin, one hundred priests with silver staffs in hand—was every man, woman, and child in the land there to accompany him?

The heads of the Torah academies called out, "May you go in peace and return in peace!"

"Amen!" answered the multitude. Thousands of voices resounded off the stone walls of the Temple.

The noise was so great that birds in flight fell to the ground.

Yehudah stood in awe.

❦

"There he is, Kimchit! There he is!" cried a friend struggling to peer over the crowd. Yom Kippur was nearing its end and the high priest had completed his last service of the day. "Yes, I see him! I'm sure of it!" she continued. "He's the only one wearing the golden breastplate, isn't he? I can see him even from back here!"

She looked at Kimchit sitting quietly within the large Temple courtyard. Except for the prayers she whispered without stop, the old woman showed no sign that it was her son who had just emerged from the Holy of Holies alive.

"Come on, Kimchit! Climb up here so you can see," urged her friend. "It's not every day you can see your youngest son wearing the robes of the high priest."

"May he live and be well," smiled Kimchit. "I will see him soon enough."

Stars filled the sky with light as thousands of worshippers dressed in white and bearing wax torches surged forth from the Temple. Though they had all been fasting since the previous evening, no one even thought of returning home before kissing the high priest's hands.

Kimchit was pushed along with the throngs. Soon it was her turn to pass before her son.

"Mother..." said Yehudah hoarsely.

"You did well," Kimchit whispered. "We'll talk later. Now you must attend to the people."

"Seven sons..." marveled a sage sitting across from Yehudah at the celebration later that night. "What special merit has enabled your mother to see all seven of her sons serve as high priest?"

"Why don't you ask her?" Shimon ben Kimchit interjected before his brother could utter a word.

The sages at the table grew silent. All heads turned to the next room, where Kimchit stood talking happily with her many well-wishers.

"Yes," agreed Yehudah. "Why don't you ask her?"

❦

"What did she say?" the sages asked their emissary eagerly when he returned to the table. "Did she give you an explanation?"

"She said something," began the young scholar in confusion. "But I can't say I understand her answer. 'It's because of my hair,' she told me. 'Since my wedding day, even the beams of my house have not seen my hair.'"

The sages looked at one another in surprise. Was this the act that had earned Kimchit seven high priests? Covering her hair? Surely no married woman would be seen in public with her head uncovered!

"But she spoke of the beams of her house," ventured one rabbi. "Not only has no person ever seen her hair, but even the very beams supporting her house.... That means even when no one is watching—"

"But isn't a woman permitted to uncover her hair in the privacy of her home?" protested another scholar.

"Permitted, yes," countered the first. "There is no prohibition when she is alone. But isn't there an added virtue in acting with dignity in the presence of God? Can one ever escape His scrutiny?"

"My mother has always kept herself concealed," Shimon confirmed. "She has always taught us, 'God formed our bodies like precious jewels. If you have a diamond, do you parade it in the street?' Perhaps that is why we, her sons, have been privileged to enter the most hidden place of all, the Holy of Holies, where only God's presence is found."

"Of course!" exclaimed one of the sages, remembering the words of King David: "'All the dignity of the king's daughter remains within; she will be adorned with squares of gold.' It has been taught for generations that the golden squares refer to the golden breastplate that will adorn her son."

"But what about other Jewish women?" a young scholar pressed him. "Don't they all know the words of King David? Aren't many of them modest even within the confines of their own homes? Is only Kimchit scrupulous in this matter?"

Yehudah cleared his throat and looked across the large hall to the room where his mother was receiving an endless stream of women.

"Perhaps you yourselves have answered the question," he began softly. "All Jewish women know that modesty brings one special merit. They all hope to be blessed with distinguished sons. But my mother never set out to make us high priests. She behaved modestly only for the sake of honoring her Creator, in Whose image she was formed. She never forgot for a moment that she stood in His presence."

The brothers nodded in agreement. "Yes, Yehudah is right. She never thought of reward."

"Maybe that's why her name is Kimchit," smiled an older sage. "Kimchit means 'flour,' and the flour of Kimchit is different from any other. Most flour is mixed with coarse bran, like the personal motives mixed into most people's behavior. But the flour of Kimchit is finely sifted; her actions are done purely for the sake of Heaven."

Kimchit tried to keep herself concealed, but the sages have revealed her greatness for posterity. Throughout the Talmud's myriad pages of law and ethical teachings, men are referred to by their fathers' names. But Shimon and Yehudah ben Kimchit will forever be known as the sons of their righteous mother.

Vayikra Rabbah 20:11
Yoma 47a* and *Ben Yehoyada* ad loc.

*Author's note: Unlike *Vayikra Rabbah*, the Gemara's version of this story identifies Kimchit's two sons as Yishmael and Yosef, not Shimon and Yehudah.

בטח בה לב בעלה....

Her husband's heart
relies on her....

*T*he wisdoms of women have built her house."
This refers to the wife of On ben Pelet.

[Why was On ben Pelet numbered among] the
sons of Reuven? Because he saw [ra'ah] and
understood [heivin].

(Sanhedrin 110a)

This means that he saw and understood that
his wife's words were correct.

(Maharsha ad loc.)

On the Doorpost of Her Home

*O*n's daughter gingerly placed one foot upon the
path leading to the well, as if testing its firm-
ness. Could it be that only yesterday, on this
very spot, the earth had opened up its jaws and swallowed men, women, and children alive?

Life seemed to be returning to normal, but she
wondered if the Israelite camp would ever be the same.
This was how Noach must have felt when he first
stepped out onto dry land; how Lot would have felt if
he'd ever returned to the ruins of Sodom; how the
Jews must have felt gazing back at the tranquil waters of the Red Sea. Not a memory of Noach's way-
ward generation; not a remnant of Lot's neighbors;
not a trace of Egypt's horsemen. And not a pot or
comb or sandal strap from all the wealth of Korach.

She felt that the ground beneath her feet was no

longer mere earth. It was the back of a sleeping beast that had once been roused to fury. The sky gazed down impassively, giving no hint of the upheaval it had so recently witnessed. But the morning stillness carried echoes of thunder, and in every face she saw the eyes of a survivor.

Overnight, her own family had acquired a new identity. From now on her father would be known as On ben Pelet—Mourner, Son of Wonders. And there was no question that he was the most wondrous survivor of them all.

As she approached the well, On's daughter thought back to the last time she had been there....

Although she and her mother had risen early that morning, there were already many others before them. The young girl had dipped a goatskin flask into the water and placed it on her shoulder. Then she filled a second flask for her mother to carry.

"Have you heard what Korach's been saying?" asked a tall, fair-skinned Levite women. "He claims that Moshe is inventing his own commandments."

A young bride from the tribe of Shimon nodded as she lowered her bucket. "My husband says nothing could be sillier than some of the laws he has been taught. Take the laws of fringes, for instance. Must a man attach a blue fringe to his garment even when the garment itself is completely blue?"

"And what about the *mezuzah*?" added the Levite woman. "Korach asked why a house full of Torah scrolls still needs the piece of parchment with the words of the Shema posted on its doorpost. Wouldn't there be holy words to spare in such a place?"

On's wife tugged on her daughter's sleeve and pulled her away from the well.

"That you should hear such foolishness!" she shuddered. "That such nonsense should be spoken in this camp! Korach obviously wants to discredit Moshe and claim the high priesthood for himself. But if he is already mentioning the fringes, he should remember what they stand for.

"The numerical value of the word '*tzitzit*,' fringe, is 600, and each one contains 8 threads and 5 knots. That's 613 all together, symbolizing the 613 commandments given to us as a nation. No one person was meant to do them all. The priest cannot fulfill the obligations of the Levite, nor can the Levite do those of the Israelite. A woman may not perform the duties of men, but neither may a man take on the laws of a woman. God has created each one of us as a limb in the body of Israel. Do the eyes fight with the tongue over who should speak? Do the hands push aside the feet and try to walk? We must all be true to our God-given essence. Only then can the Jewish people flourish."

"But, Mother," the young girl asked, "what about the blue thread? Is it true that even if the whole *tallit* is spun from blue wool, it still needs an extra blue string?"

"Yes," nodded her mother. "That's the whole point! If the entire *tallit* is blue, the single thread is what stands out and attracts attention. When we see the blue string it should remind us of the blue sea. The sea, in turn, is a reflection of the blue skies, which lift our thoughts to our Father in Heaven.

"Everyone is talking about how silly the blue thread is! If only they would realize its message: Stop focusing on your own self. Put aside your petty desires. Turn your eyes upward, and let all your actions be for the sake of Heaven."

"And the *mezuzah*, Mother? On the doorposts of our house?"

"The *mezuzah* also serves as a reminder. When we look up at it as we pass through the door, we remember the words of God written inside, and we are protected."

"And you know what else?" smiled the girl as she slipped her hand into her mother's palm. "The *mezuzah* contains the words, 'And you shall teach them to your children....'"

As they continued walking, they saw a crowd gathering around the Tent of Meeting. Soon they drew closer and heard voices shouting:

"He makes himself king!"

"And his brother the high priest!"

"And don't forget his nephews...they're the priests!"

She heard her mother gasp. "It is bad. Very bad..." the woman whispered. "We must have no part of it. Let's go home the other way."

They turned to go, but suddenly they heard a familiar voice in the crowd. In disbelief, they turned to take a second look. Yes, there he was, among the rebels....

❦

Hours later, her mother was still trembling. "Your father, too? How can it be?" she kept asking as she stared blankly towards the opening of the tent.

"Don't worry, Mother. You can stop him. Just explain to him that this rebellion makes no sense. He'll see that you're right."

But her mother shook her head. "How can you be so sure?"

Just then On appeared in the doorway. And just as suddenly the girl saw a change come over her mother. Like creases falling from a shaken cloth, the lines of concern fell from her features. She greeted her husband calmly and did not bring up the rebellion until later that evening.

"Well, it's time you knew," shrugged On. "I'll do as I see fit and there's nothing you can say to change my mind."

"Fine," conceded his wife. "I'll agree with you. Let's say Korach is right. Let's say Moshe *did* choose Aharon because he's his brother. What difference does it make to you? What do you gain by taking part in the revolt? Korach is a Levite, but you are from the tribe of Reuven. Even if he becomes the high priest, you will still be only a disciple."

On was silent for a few minutes.

"It's true," he agreed, "I have nothing to gain for myself. But shouldn't I fight for justice? Is it right to stand by silently while Moshe takes advantage of his position?"

On's daughter looked at her mother with concern. Clearly, no amount of arguing would convince her father that Moshe was beyond reproach. Would her parents get caught up in an endless debate?

Her mother just nodded. "I don't like to see injustice any more than you do. But I know that there's a Judge in the heavens. If Moshe is really abusing his power, God will take care of it."

"But we are commanded to eradicate evil from our midst!"

"Yes, but only when you're sure that it's evil. I wouldn't want to be the one to make such an assumption about men as holy as Moshe and Aharon."

On began to look uncertain.

"But Korach is no fool," he said. "And he is prepared to fight it out."

"Good," said his wife. "Let him fight. He hopes to become the leader of Israel, or at least the high priest. I still don't see what you have to gain."

"You're right. Why should I fight someone else's battle?"

"*And* put yourself in danger," On's wife added softly.

"Yes, there is a certain danger involved. I don't think the Almighty will take this matter lightly.... But what can I do? I have given Korach my word. I have sworn to join them in their rebellion tomorrow morning, when they go to burn the incense."

Mother and daughter glanced at each other in horror.

"Burn the incense?!" On's wife cried out. "Korach and his men intend to burn the incense? Don't they know that only priests are permitted to do that?"

"That was the test Moshe proposed. And they have accepted it. They believe they will succeed."

The woman shook her head slowly. "These men are going to their deaths. That is where all this is heading." Then she looked up in alarm. "And you swore you'd go with them? You gave them your word?!"

On had turned deathly white. He nodded but did not meet her eyes.

❦

When On awoke the next morning, his wife was waiting for him with a large goblet of wine.

"Have a drink," she urged. "Go back to sleep."

Every time he awoke she poured him another glass, until eventually he was lost in a drunken stupor.

"Come," she motioned to her daughter. "Let's make sure your father is not disturbed today."

She took a stool and sat herself down at the entrance of the tent. Then she untied her kerchief and began to comb out her thick, black hair.

"Mother!" the young girl shrieked. "What on earth are you doing? Come inside quickly."

"No," her mother replied calmly, handing her a second comb. "I am saving your father's life. He has sworn to join the rebels when they call for him. But I will make sure they never get near him."

On's daughter stared at her mother for many moments. Finally she sat down beside her and slowly loosened her braid.

It was not long before one of Korach's messengers appeared to summon On. As he neared the tent, he caught sight of the two women and clapped a hand over his eyes. How could he approach them with their hair exposed? And so he turned back.

Another messenger was sent. And after him, another. But still the women sat there, combing out their hair.

Suddenly they heard a great ripping sound. The earth began to quake and then they saw Moshe running past.

"Away! Away!" he shouted. "Get away from the tent of Korach!" Racing back and forth, he seized small children in his massive arms and pushed them out of the Levite encampment. "Run!" he cried. "Quickly!"

And then it happened. The earth came alive and opened up its mighty lips. Entire families—their clothing, jewels, furniture, cattle...all gulped down into the bowels of the deep.

On's wife sat frozen beside her daughter, her hand still raised to her head, her fingers still clutching the comb. From afar, the women's eyes fell upon a deep chasm pushing through the camp—and hurtling right towards them.

Suddenly the earth beneath their tent began to shift and crack open. Raising his head groggily, On peered over the side of his bed. Down, down went the endless chasm.

On's wife jumped up and gripped the edge of the bed. "Master of the Universe!" she cried out. "On has separated himself from Korach's rebellion. Do not hurl him into the abyss with them. Spare his life and he shall never speak against Moshe again!"

With the eyes of a dead man, On gaped incredulously as his wife fought for his life. Her prayers were all that stood between him and annihilation.

Slowly, the ground began to shift back, and the crevice closed.

❧

It was many hours before On's spirit returned to his body. He lay limply on his bed, his muscles melted from fright.

"You must get up and go to Moshe!" insisted his wife towards evening. "You must throw yourself at his feet and beg his forgiveness!"

On leaned back on his pillow and covered his face with his hands. "I cannot stand before him," he wept. "I am too ashamed. How could I have been such a fool?"

On's wife looked at him gravely. "I have saved your body," she declared. "Now I shall try to save your soul."

On's daughter rose up and accompanied her mother to the Levite encampment. They fell to the ground before Moshe's tent and cried out bitterly, "What will become of our husband and father, who is too ashamed to ask your forgiveness?"

Moshe stepped forward and followed them back to their home. "Arise from your bed," the leader called to On, "that the Almighty may forgive you!"

After Moshe left the tent, On turned to his wife in confusion. "He is the one I have wronged. Why did he say the Almighty should forgive me?"

On's wife was silent for a few moments. Finally she said softly, "It is true that you sinned against Moshe. But surely he bears no ill will. A God-fearing person understands that whatever suffering people cause him comes from Above for his own benefit.

"But when you hurt another person, you also sin against God. Moshe is not at liberty to absolve you of this transgression. God Himself must see your regret and know that you will not repeat the sin. You must beg His forgiveness."

On lowered his head in shame. If he had been unable to face Moshe, how could he face God?

"Go ahead," urged his wife. "God will forgive."

Surely the Almighty did forgive On ben Pelet. And just as surely, He blessed On's wife, who sat at the doorpost of her home and protected it from evil.

Tanchuma, Korach 11
Midrash HaGadol, Bemidbar 16:32
Sanhedrin 109b and Maharsha ad loc.
Rabbi Yaakov Neiman, *Darkei Mussar,*
   Korach, p. 193

...ושלל לא יחסר.

...and he shall lack
no fortune.

*R*abbi Shimon's wife chose to live in abject poverty in order that her husband would be rewarded for studying Torah nonetheless.

(Kochvei Or, chap. 8)

❧

The Very Last Jewel

Rabbi Shimon bar Chalafta's wife placed three large, round matzot on the plate in the center of the table. "Will this night be that different from all other nights?" she asked herself.

There would be soup—again. But she had been careful not to water it down as much as usual. She had added the meat bone the butcher had saved for her, and turned three precious eggs into delicate, thin noodles.

"And tonight," she reminded herself as she surveyed her mismatched tableware, which seemed to gain a few more cracks every year, "tonight we're having matzo. That will certainly be different."

She busied herself with tidying up the dining room and arranging the chairs. It was no problem finding time to set the table, for the little cooking she could do had been finished hours ago.

After all the place settings were ready, she turned to the head of the table and ran her fingers over the fine lines etched in Rabbi Shimon's special cedarwood chair. It had been in the family for generations, gracing table after table as the place of honor for the scholarly master of the home.

No one else would dream of sitting in it.

Something else would make this night special. Throughout the year, Rabbi Shimon shared a new and creative Torah thought at every meal, but the Seder always brought out his best. This was what caused the students to crowd around their table year after year, despite the meager fare.

"It's funny," mused Rabbi Shimon's wife, covering the brittle matzot as gently as she could. "Matzo fills empty stomachs for many hours. It is a poor man's bread, the food of slaves. Yet, it has a place of honor on our Seder table every year. It symbolizes our freedom; it was the only bread we had time to bake as we hurried to the promised land. So simple, so lowly...yet we raise it so high...."

Just then, the door creaked open. Rabbi Shimon's wife looked up and blinked in disbelief.

There was her husband, keeping the door ajar with one shoulder as he pushed two crates forward with his feet and grasped overflowing packages in his arms. Bottles of sweet wine for the four cups; apples and nuts for *charoset*; enough chickens for a week of festive meals; and, peeking out from a bundle on the side, a fine piece of white lace that could only be for....

"This is wonderful, Shimon!" she exclaimed. "But where did it come from? How did you ever pay for it?"

Rabbi Shimon put down his packages and tried to catch his breath.

"I didn't," he said at last. "It was paid for by the Holy One."

"What do you mean? Tell me where it came from!" she urged, overwhelmed by curiosity.

"I was studying with Rebbi, just as I do every day," he began as he fell into his chair. "We were learning the law 'And you shall take pleasure in your festival....' The sages teach that one must provide his family with pleasure during the holiday. Most agree that this refers to wine, but Rabbi Yehudah says: 'Let the men have their pleasure and the women have theirs. The men should have wine, but the women should be given nice clothing.' Still, all maintain that there is no joy without meat and wine.

"'Wine? Meat? New clothes?' I thought. 'I can't afford any of these things.'

"As we were talking, I became aware of many voices outside the window. People were rushing about in all directions, and it seemed as if every Jew in the city of Tiberias had taken to the streets.

"'Where are they all going?' I asked.

"Rebbi looked at me for a long moment. 'The ones with money are going to buy food for the holiday,' he said gently.

"'And the ones without money?'

"'They are going to ask whoever they work for to provide for their needs,' he answered.

"I watched the people hurrying past and pondered

Rebbi's words. 'Don't I also need to buy food for the holiday?' I thought. 'Should my table have less?'

"So I rose from the bench and slipped on my coat. 'Now I, too, shall go to the One I work for,' I told Rebbi.

"I left the city at once and headed towards the caves in the surrounding hills. I stood alone, far from anyone else, and prayed that the Holy One provide for our needs. 'Master of the Universe,' I cried, 'don't let employers of flesh and blood pay better wages than You! Give Your scholars the means to honor holy days, as You Yourself have prescribed. Please don't allow them to be disgraced before their neighbors.'

"After many moments, I opened my eyes to see a stone shining in the dust at my feet. I stashed it deep in my pocket and made my way back to the study hall.

"Rebbi slowly turned the stone over in his hand and held it up to the sunlight pouring in through the window.

"'A diamond!' he exclaimed. 'Now you're a wealthy man!'

"He took three dinars out of his pocket and pressed them into my hand.

"'You have never agreed to let me help you, but now you can take my money,' he urged me. 'Buy whatever you need for the holiday, and next week we will auction off this jewel to the highest bidder.

"'You will be able to live comfortably for the rest of your life!' he added so joyfully that this seemed to be the answer to his prayers instead of mine.

"So you see," smiled Rabbi Shimon as he motioned to the produce stacked high in the corner, "the Holy One paid for all my purchases."

Rabbi Shimon's wife kept silent. It was hard for her to meet her husband's jubilant gaze.

How could she explain that she already knew her table would shine with a special glow on Pesach night...that she did not wish for whatever might be found on any other table...that she had always felt truly rich? And how could she tell him that this very jewel might prove their undoing?

"What have you done, Shimon?" she finally cried. "What have you done? You have provided well for our table here on earth. But shall our table in the next world be lacking?"

The smile on Rabbi Shimon's face quickly faded. He looked over at the purchases that had delighted him minutes earlier. Now they seemed an unbearable burden.

"What should I do?" he asked quietly.

"There is only one thing you *can* do," said his wife. "Take back the food. Take back the money. And take back the diamond."

Rabbi Shimon hurried back to the marketplace, returned all his purchases, and brought the three dinars back to Rebbi.

"Didn't you buy food for the holiday?" Rebbi asked in surprise. "There are only a few hours left before the holiday begins and here you are handing me back my money!"

"I did buy food," Rabbi Shimon explained. "I bought enough for the entire week, but my wife advised me to take it back."

A cloud of disappointment descended on the sage's features.

"Perhaps I should speak with her," he said.

Before long, Rabbi Shimon's wife was standing before Rebbi outside the study hall.

"Why are you causing your good husband pain?" Rebbi demanded.

"Pain?" she asked incredulously. "What of the pain he will feel in the World to Come, when he finds that his table has one less jewel on it than yours?"

"Surely I can give him one of mine," said Rebbi.

Rabbi Shimon's wife raised her head and glanced into the study hall. Pairs of scholars argued loudly at every table, each absorbed in their own world of study, oblivious to anything else.

"With all due respect," she whispered as she gazed down at the floor, "I do not know if we will see one another in the afterlife. I have heard that each soul becomes a world unto itself."

Rabbi Shimon's wife had no doubt that Rebbi was more learned than her husband. But there was one facet of her husband's Torah that he could never match. For Rebbi was a wealthy man and studied in comfort. He never had reason to worry about money. Rabbi Shimon was destitute, however, and suffered greatly to devote himself to Torah.

His wife understood that the greater one's effort in learning, the greater one's reward; and Torah learned in poverty is a hundred times more valuable than Torah learned in affluence.

She recognized at once that the diamond would have imperiled this great merit, for no longer would her husband's Torah be acquired amid hardship. The same study that he engaged in today would be robbed of its unique triumph tomorrow.

How could Rebbi ever hope to replace this loss? Could he offer a merit that he himself did not possess?

Rebbi was silent for a long time.

"Yes," he sighed at last. "I believe you are right."

Rabbi Shimon headed to the distant caves for the second time that day. He closed his eyes in prayer and waited. Finally, he looked down at the dust by his feet.

The diamond was gone. He was penniless once more.

But Rabbi Shimon knew that it would be his again one day. For his wife had zealously guarded his wealth. In the world of truth, it would be waiting for him...right down to the very last jewel.

Ruth Rabbah 3:4
Rabbi Yitzchak Blazer, *Kochvei Or*, chap. 8

גמלתהו טוב ולא רע...

She brings him good
and not harm....

*H*e kept him as the apple of his eye."
God guards those who trust in Him
as a person guards the apple of his eye.

(Tanchuma, Haazinu 9)

A Sacred Trust

"No more men shall die because of me," thought the young widow as she sat in mourning once again.

Uncovering the mirror that had been concealed for seven days, she brushed the ashes from her brow and studied her reflection carefully.

"No," she decided. "Better I remain alone for the rest of my life."

It was many days before she stepped outside her home. She packed away the bright clothes she loved and shut the drawer where she had placed her jewels. Dressed in black, she looked much older than her years. But up close, her face was as lovely as ever.

Early one evening the young widow heard cries of joy coming from the front room. Putting down her needlework, she went to see.

Before she entered the room, she heard her father cry out: "Blessed is He who revives the dead!"

Her heart skipped a beat and she stopped in confusion. Only upon seeing her cousin standing in the doorway did she realize that her father had pronounced the customary blessing upon meeting a long lost friend.

"It has been years since we have seen you!" he continued joyfully.

The young woman stayed in the shadows and studied her cousin. Was it only due to his long journey that he looked so weary? The last time she had seen him, she'd been peeking through the branches of the weeping willow where she was playing house. They were both children then, with their parents visiting in the *sukkah* nearby. She would hardly have recognized him now....

His eyes met hers and she looked quickly away. Drawing her long, black shawl around her, she turned and headed back to her room.

Only at dinner did the young widow venture out of her self-imposed isolation to sit wordlessly at the table. As her cousin spoke, she learned that it was not just his journey that had worn him down. His father had fallen on hard times and it was a struggle for him to feed his ten children. The boy looked at his younger brothers and sisters and decided, "I shall travel to my uncle and see how he is after all these years. Perhaps he has fared better than we have. Perhaps he can help."

As soon as the story was heard, a messenger was sent on horseback with a purse of silver coins for the starving family.

❦

The young man stayed on in his relatives' home, and before long his uncle had shown him around his business, discussing his concerns with his insightful nephew and listening to his advice.

But no matter how close he became to his uncle, he could not coax more than a few words from his beautiful cousin before she once again vanished into her room.

One day the young man found his uncle alone in the garden.

"I have a request," he began. "Do not refuse me."

His uncle looked at him in surprise. "You know you can ask whatever you want," he told him.

"First you must promise not to say 'no,'" the nephew persisted. "Promise me."

"Very well, I promise you," smiled the older man. "Now what is it?"

The boy stepped back and brushed against the willow tree. He took a deep breath, straightened his shoulders, and said in a strong voice, "I ask only one thing. Give me your daughter for a wife."

A tremor ran through the old man's body. The blood drained from his face and his eyes filled with fear.

"Had you asked for all my wealth, I would not have refused you, but no, my son!" he whispered hoarsely. "No! Do not ask me that."

The young man stared in confusion. "Why are you so frightened?"

"There is something I have never told you," explained his uncle as he lowered his head in shame. "I am being punished for my sins...." He paused and slowly spoke each word. "My daughter is not a widow for the first time. She has already lost three husbands...all on their wedding night...."

The afternoon shadows grew longer as he shared the bitter story with his nephew. But the boy was not deterred.

"If it is my time to die, I will die whether I marry her or not. And if it is not my time, what harm can come to me?"

His uncle shook his head sadly. "I wish it were that simple," he said. "But Heaven seems to have decreed that my daughter must suffer. Her husbands may not have been destined to die young, but when they married my daughter their fate became entwined with hers. They may have been taken from this world to fulfill a decree against her."

The young man raised his head and looked directly into his uncle's haunted eyes.

"I wish to marry her all the same," he declared.

His uncle put an arm around his shoulders. "Look," he said gently, "I know you're worried about your family back home. If it's a dowry you're after, you have my word: leave her alone, don't think of her again, and I will give you all the wealth you desire. You are a good boy, you have a lot to look forward to. Please take my advice. Don't put yourself in danger."

"But you forget," said the young man. "You gave me your word."

❦

His uncle had no choice but to agree to his proposal. But convincing the girl was another matter.

"Master of the Universe!" the young widow wept when she was told of her cousin's desire. "Take my own life this very moment, but don't let another man die because of me."

She refused to consider marriage. In truth, she had grown to love the boy during his short stay in their home. But how could she become his wife?

"Isn't it better to see you alive than to make you mine and lose you forever?" she asked him.

The young man spoke to her softly, convincing her. "Does God want you to stop living?" he asked her. "Does He want you to give up? No, there must be a way...."

The date was set and preparations began. Friends and neighbors milled about her parents' home in speechless trepidation. For days before the wedding, they carried in trays of honey cake and kegs of cider. But the thought on every mind was the same: Would this food soon be served to those coming to comfort the mourners?

The bride herself was nowhere to be seen. She had secluded herself in her room, putting the finishing touches on her gown.

"Don't You place the paths of life and death before each person?" she cried out to God as she sewed another pearl onto the collar. "Then let me choose life!"

❧

After the wedding feast, when all the guests had returned home, the bride slipped away from her family and locked herself in her childhood room. Here she felt safe and protected. Here no evil could befall her.

"The world was created for each individual," she thought as she poured out her heart in prayer. "It must have a place for me as well. If God loves me and wants me to succeed, then I must fight with all my soul."

Suddenly, she heard an urgent knock.

"Open the door!" called her new husband. "Open the door! Let me speak to you!"

"What's the matter?" she cried when she found him gasping for air in the entranceway.

The young man lifted his eyes and looked for a long moment at his new bride, trying to freeze her image in his mind. "I have come to ask your permission before I go," he said softly.

"No," she trembled. "It can't be...."

"I just heard the voice of the angel of death," explained the boy. "He has come to take my life.

"'Please,' I begged him, 'give me just one year. Or even six months....'

"'No,' he shook his head, 'I cannot.'

"'Then just one month,' I pleaded, 'or at least the seven days of the wedding celebration....'

"'I cannot give you even one more day,' the angel insisted. 'Your time has come.'

"'Then, please, I ask you, wait here until I take leave of my wife. Let me ask her permission before I set out on my journey.'

"'This one request I shall grant you,' the angel nodded, 'but go and come back quickly.'"

The girl drew her husband into the room. "You stay here," she said calmly. "I shall go and speak for myself."

The young bride stepped out into the night and raised her eyes heavenward.

"You have taken three men from me," she cried out, "but this one I will fight for! I have new evidence to use in his defense and it is found in Your own Torah."

Her last words echoed in the night. She looked up at the cloudless sky as if waiting for permission to continue.

"The Torah says: 'When a man takes a new wife, he shall not go out to war or embark on any journey; he shall be free in his home for one year and shall rejoice with his wife....'

"You are true and Your word is true," the young bride asserted. "But if You take my husband, the Torah will become a lie."

She trembled at the words she had spoken. The air around her was still. No sound could be heard in the bushes. It seemed as if the entire universe was holding its breath, waiting for the verdict to be handed down.

The young bride returned to her room, where her husband waited.

"Do not fear," she told him, closing the door behind her with a silent prayer.

🌱

The bride's parents sat weeping in a nearby room. Hours passed in anguish. Then, at midnight, they rose from the floor and went out to the garden. Beneath the willow they dug a fresh grave for their new son-in-law.

The next morning they stood before the door in dread. They pictured the terrible look they would once again see in their daughter's eyes. They imagined the cries of terror, the painful weeping, and finally the resigned silence of one who has endured more than the heart can bear. How would they find the words to comfort her?

Suddenly the grim silence was broken by laughter from within. The father and mother stood in shock for many frozen moments until the new bride and her husband opened the door and their daughter fell into their arms.

"You were both determined to fight for life," whispered the father as they held her tightly. "You put your trust in God's justice, and God guards those who trust in Him."

Tanchuma, Haazinu 9

...ממרחק תביא לחמה.

...from afar she brings
her bread.

*R*abbi Chanina's wife's trust in God was so great that she saw no difference between the natural and the miraculous.

(Rabbi Chaim Shmuelevitz, *Sichot Mussar*, part 3, essay 16)

He Who Told the Oil to Burn

*R*abbi Chanina ben Dosa's wife picked up a stick and added it to the bundle under her arm. It was Friday afternoon, when other women were busy kneading dough and braiding challah, carving meat and peeling carrots. But here she was, gathering moist twigs to throw into her oven. With little food in her house, there was not much cooking to be done; but at least when smoke rose from all the other homes, it would rise from hers as well.

This procedure was essential to her Sabbath preparations. "If I cannot satisfy my family's hunger," she reasoned, "I can at least satisfy my neighbors' curiosity. If I cannot honor my loved ones with delicious food, I will honor them by guarding their dignity."

Looking at her smoking chimney, who would suspect that she had no chickens to roast or challahs to bake?

"I wish I didn't have to concern myself with appearances," sighed Rabbi Chanina's wife. "But some people measure wealth by sacks of grain instead of acts of kindness. They would surely see things differently if they lived with a man like my husband, who can call upon God's miracles at will...."

She remembered the Friday afternoon when her daughter had accidentally filled the candlesticks with vinegar instead of oil. It was too close to sundown to refill them. Would they have no light to greet the holy day? A cloud of gloom enveloped the girl as she realized her mistake. But Rabbi Chanina would not have his daughter welcome the Sabbath Queen with sadness. "The day of rest is almost upon us!" he told his family. "It is a taste of the World to Come. Vinegar, oil—what difference does it make?"

He smiled at the girl and added, "He Who told oil to burn can also tell vinegar to burn."

And indeed, the flames burned brightly not just that night but all through the next day.

Many such miracles took place in her home, yet Rabbi Chanina's wife knew that all of life was miraculous. "Isn't it a miracle that the human mind can even come close to understanding God's holy words? Isn't it a miracle that we have the ability to live in this physical world according to His laws?"

And as she fried a few coarse pancakes for their evening meal, she knew it was a miracle that her underfed family remained healthy and strong.

Gradually, she became aware of low voices outside her door. "I know these people don't have a crumb in their house," one of her neighbors was whispering to passersby. "So what's all this smoke from?"

This murmuring was followed by an insistent knock on the door. "Hello! Hello! Are you home?" she heard her neighbor calling.

Then she heard the door creak open. Was this woman actually going to walk into her house uninvited? Would she stop at nothing to verify her suspicions? And what would she do after searching the kitchen and finding it bare, and after opening the oven and finding nothing but charred twigs?

Rabbi Chanina's wife could well imagine: her neighbor would run to tell her friends, who would then waste no time in telling *their* friends what a disgrace it was that the great rabbi let his family go hungry, and that they covered up their shame by burning sticks....

Yet Rabbi Chanina's wife was certain that God would not let a life of Torah be denigrated. She had done all she could to protect her husband's honor. The rest was in God's hands.

As her neighbor entered, Rabbi Chanina's wife calmly walked into her bedroom.

Her neighbor closed the door behind her and headed for the kitchen.

"A holy man, a Torah scholar," she muttered to herself, "and look at the way they live. At least my husband makes an honest living...." Suddenly, her eyes opened wide in astonishment. For a moment she was speechless. What was this? A large bowl on the counter overflowing with dough? And made of the very finest flour? She swung open the oven door and turned red with embarrassment. She had been disproven.

"So my neighbor is not as bad off as I imagined,"

she admitted grudgingly as she surveyed the trays of bread. Then she raised her voice: "Come take care of your challahs before they burn."

Rabbi Chanina's wife hurried out of the bedroom, a spatula in her hand.

"It's a good thing you came now," called her neighbor. "Your beautiful loaves are about to turn black."

"I just went to fetch my spatula," smiled Rabbi Chanina's wife as she matter-of-factly extracted her bread from the oven.

God has endowed us all with free choice. Our challenge is to see God's hand in our lives, although He keeps Himself hidden. Surely if we saw Him clearly, or witnessed open miracles, we would not be rewarded for our choices.

Rabbi Chanina's wife chose to recognize God's involvement in everything, and everything filled her with wonder. She saw His hand miraculously igniting her oil every Sabbath eve. When her wicks blazed with vinegar, was it any more amazing? He Who told oil to burn could also tell vinegar to burn. He could make challahs out of flour or out of sticks. The hands of God—the hidden and the revealed—were one and the same to the wife of Rabbi Chanina ben Dosa.

Only such a woman could live amidst miracles.

Taanit 24b, 25a
Rabbi Simchah Zissel Ziv, *Chochmah U'Mussar*, vol. II, p. 271
Rabbi Chaim Shmuelevitz, *Sichot Mussar*, part 3, essay 16

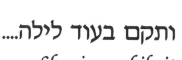

ותקם בעוד לילה....

She rises while it
is yet night....

*R*abban Yochanan ben Zakai had five students.... He recounted their praises.... [Concerning] Rabbi Yehoshua [he said]: Happy is the one who bore him.

(Pirkei Avot 2:10-11)

The men come [to Jerusalem for the mitzvah of hakhel] to learn, and the women come to hear. Why do the small children come? To grant reward to those who bring them.

(Chagigah 3a)

First Impressions

*T*ell me the story about Mama," pleaded Yehoshua as he climbed onto his grandmother's knees. "Tell about when I was a baby in her belly."

The old woman laughed and threw up her arms in mock despair. "I must have told you that story a hundred times!"

Yehoshua stuck his thumb in his mouth and burrowed deeper into her lap. "Just one more time, Grandma."

"Well, it all started the winter before you were born. It was the coldest weather in years. Snow in Jerusalem! And it didn't melt right away as it usually does. No, this year the snow stood in huge drifts in the roads.

"People stayed indoors as much as they could.

Only when it was time to pray would they venture out, each one heading for the nearest synagogue and then hurrying back home.

"But not your mother! Early every morning she would pull her coat around her big belly and set out on her rounds. I would follow her to the door and beg her to stay home. 'How can you go out in such weather?' I would scold her. 'And in your condition? The streets are slippery! What if you fall on the ice? If you won't think of yourself, at least think of the baby!'

"'Mother,' she would say, 'I **am** thinking of the baby.' Then she would pull an extra scarf around her head and hurry out of the house. I always knew I wouldn't see her for hours."

"Tell where she would go," urged the young boy.

"Your mother would go to every synagogue in the city, starting with the sunrise services and ending with the late risers. Arriving towards the end of the morning prayers, she would stand outside in the cold, waiting for the rabbis to come out."

"And tell what she would ask the rabbis, Grandma."

"Oh, yes," the old woman smiled. "Your mama would stop the rabbis and say, 'Please pray for mercy for the child I carry. Pray that he be granted wisdom!'"

"And about my cradle...."

His grandmother shifted him to her other knee. "You don't let me forget a word, do you?" she marveled. "When you were born, we thought your mama would finally get some rest. But after a few weeks, she resumed her rounds, this time with you bundled up as well. 'Where are you heading now?' we all asked her. 'To the study hall,' she said. 'What for?' I *demanded. 'And why drag the baby?' But she just lifted up your cradle and said, 'It is for him that I'm going.'*

"And so she would go to the study hall and set up your cradle near where the scholars were learning. And all day long, holy words of Torah would fill your ears."

"And tell why Mama did it," pressed Yehoshua.

"Your mama did it so that you would grow up with a love of Torah and become a great scholar," smiled his grandmother. "May it be God's will...."

Rabbi Yehoshua ben Chananiah shaded his eyes from the midday glare as he watched Rabbi Yochanan ben Beroka and Rabbi Elazar ben Chisma heading down the road. He had hoped they would come. What better way to enjoy the holiday than by learning Torah with his sharpest students?

"So teach me something new," Rabbi Yehoshua said eagerly while serving them fruit and cake.

"But we are your students," protested Rabbi Yochanan. "We drink of your waters like streams fed by a mighty river. What could we possibly teach you?"

Rabbi Yehoshua impatiently waved away this praise. "In the course of learning Torah, one cannot help but uncover new ideas. Who lectured this Sabbath in the academy?"

"Rabbi Elazar ben Azariah," answered Rabbi Yochanan.

"And what topic did he speak about?" Rabbi Yehoshua probed.

Rabbi Yochanan was not sure how to speak before his master. Would he properly convey the words of one great sage to another?

Rabbi Elazar ben Chisma came to his assistance. "He spoke about *hakhel*, the commandment to assemble all the people to listen to the king read from the Torah," he began. "Rabbi Elazar observed, 'It is clear why the men and women should come to hear. They can listen and learn. But why must the children come?' And then he answered his own question: 'In order to grant reward to those who bring them.'"

"To grant reward to those who bring them?" asked Rabbi Yehoshua. "Isn't that a strange answer! If the children cannot grasp what is being taught, what is the benefit of them being there? And why should those who bring them be rewarded?"

Rabbi Yochanan cleared his throat and volunteered hesitantly, "Perhaps that is exactly the point. Parents are rewarded for bringing their children because it *is* beneficial for them to hear Torah. Even though they have no understanding, the holy words leave an impression in their hearts. They carve out grooves for themselves, like the outline of a puzzle piece. Later, when these children are old enough to study, the wisdom of the Torah is absorbed much more easily into their hearts."

"Ah..." sighed Rabbi Yehoshua. "Such a precious jewel you had in your hand! And you wished to deprive me of it?"

His disciples looked at him in surprise.

"You see," explained Rabbi Yehoshua softly, "no one ever understood my mother. They shook their heads when they saw her going from one synagogue to another, from one study hall to the next. 'Why go to so much trouble?' they asked her. 'What effect can it have on the baby in your womb or the child in your arms?' And all these years I wondered if they were right. Did the words of Torah I absorbed in the cradle really make an impression on me?

"But now I understand her great wisdom. My mother knew that her efforts would not be in vain. She knew that the holy words would be engraved upon my heart, and that my first impressions would last forever."

Chagigah 3a and Rashi, Ben Yehoyada, and Chiddushei Geonim ad loc.
Jerusalem Talmud, Yevamot 9
Avot 2:8 and Rashi ad loc.
Avot DeRabbi Natan 14 and Binyan Yeho-shua ad loc.
Rabbi Simchah Zissel Ziv, Or Rashaz, vol. 1, p. 169

זממה שדה ותקחהו....

She envisions a field
and acquires it....

*W*hat is mine and yours is due to her.

(Ketubot 63a)

Tending Her Garden

Rachel sat in the morning sun, sorting through a large tray of rice. "If I start this now," she thought as she tossed out a small, black pebble, "I can have it ready by the time Akiva comes home."

She imagined her husband off at school, forming the alphabet carefully on his slate for the first time: *aleph, beit, gimmel....* Today the block letters; tomorrow the script, a little army of letters marching before him day after day, waving their flags and crowns. And soon he would see them forming words, spelling out secret codes, relaying vital information.

Rachel sighed as she thought of all the years Akiva had not known how to read. Whatever Torah he'd managed to learn had been gathered in bits and pieces, glimpsed through a haze.

She scattered another handful of rice and then

heard the clang of the gate swinging open.

Rachel looked up in surprise.

"Akiva! You're back so early. Didn't you go to learn?"

"I went," answered Akiva wearily. "And I got as far as the schoolyard. Then I heard the children singing and I saw them through the window. They all looked so young...."

Rachel nodded. Of course he was reluctant to go inside. Why had she expected it to be easy for a grown man, probably older than the teacher himself, to join a classroom full of youngsters?

As she followed her husband into the house, she pictured him squeezing his broad frame behind a tiny desk; his legs sprawling into the aisle; his graying head towering over the others; their young voices reciting the lesson and Akiva's baritone booming above them all....

She looked at him as he hung his jacket on a peg. Even if he could ignore the children's taunting, what about the humiliation he would feel when their parents and the rest of the townspeople found out?

Akiva swung around as if her silence were accusing him.

"You're disappointed. And you have a right to be. I haven't kept my promise...."

He lowered his eyes to avoid her gaze. "You only agreed to marry me if I would study Torah. And now you've been deceived."

"Nonsense, Akiva," said Rachel firmly. "You promised to learn, and I know you will."

That night Rachel lay awake on her straw mat.

Even in the soft glow of moonlight, their small room looked spartan: an earthen floor, a rough board for a table, old rags stuffed into a broken window—there was little to remind her of the home she had so recently, and so completely, left behind. The home of her wealthy father....

She shivered and pulled her thin blanket closer. For the first time in her life, she felt unsure about the future. For the first time, she wondered if her father had been right. He had been appalled at the idea of her marrying such an ignorant man. But she had believed in the potential of Akiva, her father's laborer, whose hands were work-hardened but whose eyes held wisdom.

"Perhaps one day I will have the chance to study," he had often said to her as he watched the young men absorbed in discussions around her father's table. "There is so much I wish to know."

Rachel loved him. And she knew in her heart that he loved her, too. But he was an illiterate shepherd, and she was the wealthiest girl in the province. It was unthinkable that she should marry him.

Unthinkable to everyone but Rachel.

"There is no one I care for as much as you, Akiva," she confessed to him one day. "I would even be your wife...."

Akiva heard her hesitation.

"If only I had some money?" he broke in defensively.

"No," said Rachel quickly. "That would mean nothing to me. If only you would begin to learn Torah."

Akiva looked at her in astonishment. "Torah?" he

repeated. "I don't even know the alphabet."

"Neither does a child," said Rachel gently. "You can start at the beginning like everybody else."

"But they don't have schools for men like me."

"No, they don't," observed Rachel. "You would have to start out with the children."

Akiva sighed and looked out at the surrounding fields as if trying to see the future.

"Promise me you'll study Torah, Akiva, and I will marry you."

Akiva promised.

Rachel and Akiva were engaged in secret, but it was not long before her father found out.

And now, disowned by her family, she lived in a wooden shack, spending much of her day searching for kindling to provide some relief from the chill that blew across the floor.

Rachel closed her eyes and leaned back heavily on her bed. Until now her hopes and dreams had worked magic on her dingy surroundings. But what if Akiva's embarrassment kept him from taking that first step? What if her future would be no different from her life today? What of her dreams of a husband great in Torah learning? Would she remain a shepherd's wife forever? Was it for this that she had forsaken not only her wealth but her father's love?

Rachel knew she had to do something. But what? Argue? Threaten?

She fell asleep still wondering, but in the morning she awoke with an answer.

The sun had just begun to rise when she tiptoed

out of the house. Bringing their donkey to the front of the shack, she tied it to a post, packed moist earth all over its back, and sprinkled seeds on the dirt.

By now Akiva had come outside, where he stood watching his wife in amazement.

"What are you doing?" he asked.

"Be patient," she answered mysteriously. "You will see."

Rachel watered the donkey several times a day, turning it this way and that so the sun shone evenly on her unusual garden. She even shielded it from the evening wind. She worked with all the care of a farmer tending his choicest piece of land.

Finally the seeds sprouted and grew tall. It looked as if a bed of wild weeds were growing right out of the donkey's back.

"Akiva," called Rachel one day, "we have run out of flour. Would you please take our donkey to the marketplace and buy some?"

Akiva looked at the beast and then back at Rachel.

"Take our donkey to the market?"

"Of course," Rachel replied matter-of-factly as she unhitched the donkey from the post. "How else will you carry the flour?"

"But everyone will laugh at me," Akiva protested.

"Don't worry," answered Rachel, handing him the reins.

"Every soul was given its portion of Torah wisdom," she thought as she watched Akiva and the donkey disappear in the distance. "My husband is as obligated as anyone else to become a scholar and share his portion with the world. Can he allow people's laughter to stand in his way?"

"Now here is a sight!" someone called out as Akiva entered the marketplace. "This poor fellow can't afford to buy land so he's planted his crops on the back of his donkey!"

The shopkeepers craned their necks to see the object of derision. "What'll you do next," one of them yelled, "shave your head and put down carrots?"

"At least he'd be using his head for something useful!"

All the merchants burst out laughing.

Akiva quickly bought the flour and hurried home, thankful that his thick beard hid the shame that burned on his cheeks.

"A clown. A joke. A laughingstock. So this is what I've become instead of a scholar," he thought bitterly.

Akiva hitched the donkey to its post and hoisted the sack of flour onto his back. He did not speak a word when he entered the house, but his eyes told Rachel all she had to know. Her donkey had not passed through the marketplace unnoticed. Today her husband had become the village idiot.

"We need lentils," Rachel noted the next morning.

Akiva met her steady gaze. Didn't she know what grief this ridiculous beast had caused him?

"No," he said firmly. "I will not return to the market-place. I will not be laughed at again."

"But we have no lentils," she pressed. "Does a man cease to eat because of laughter?"

Pulling the donkey behind him, Akiva grudgingly made his way back to the market.

Every morning Rachel found a new reason to send Akiva out with the donkey. And every morning children followed him through the streets, women poked their heads out of windows, and dogs barked loudly as he passed by.

But soon winter came to the marketplace. There were leaky roofs to fix, awnings to roll out, windows to board up. The shoemakers took in their sandals and set out fur-lined boots. The rug sellers stored their straw mats and spread out carpets. The cloth merchants packed away bolts of cotton and rolled out the wools. And everyone grew indifferent to the spectacle of Akiva and his peculiar companion.

"Hmm," thought Akiva, "no one even notices anymore."

The next morning Akiva got up early and took his slate in his hand.

"I'm going to study now," he declared. "And I don't care what people will say."

"That's good," said Rachel. "If you are embarrassed, you will never learn."

Akiva squeezed himself behind a tiny desk. The teacher looked up for just a moment, then lowered his eyes. But the young pupils had no such tact. Twisting in their seats, they all tried to get a better look at this giant of a man who had come to learn among them.

Akiva gamely repeated along with the children, "*Aleph, beit, gimmel, dalet...*" but the students could not continue. Their laughter filled the classroom.

Every day Akiva climbed to the schoolhouse on the hill. As he neared the door he felt as though he were still leading the overgrown beast behind him. But when he remembered how the laughter in the marketplace had died down as surely as it had started, his courage returned.

Yes, he did look funny at his little desk. And his deep voice did sound strange among the others. He made silly mistakes. He asked simple questions. But he was never ashamed to speak, for Rachel's words echoed in his mind: "Does a man cease to eat because of laughter?"

"And just as I feed my body, I must nourish my soul," he reminded himself.

After a few weeks, the children began to look for new amusements. After all, it seemed as if the strange man was there to stay. He was learning Torah just as they were. Was it really so funny?

"Rachel could have forced me into the classroom," thought Akiva as he entered the school one morning. "She could have demanded that I keep my promise. She could have complained that her life of poverty was all for nothing. She could have called me a coward and made me feel even worse about myself than I already did.

"And even if she had assured me that I would eventually overcome the humiliation of starting out like a child, that the laughter would not last long, I would not have listened. I had to learn to endure the pain of laughter myself."

As the days went by, the letters Akiva learned did indeed begin to form words. And these words began to fill his mind with wisdom. After twenty-four years of study, he became the teacher of twenty-four thousand students. One of the greatest sages in Jewish history, his words are studied by scholars all over the world to this very day.

But few realize that Akiva's greatness is really due to the wisdom and love of his wife, Rachel, who nurtured it and watched it grow, like her donkey's garden.

Midrash HaGadol, Shemot 4:68

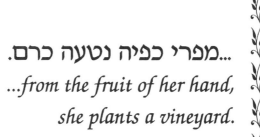

מפרי כפיה נטעה כרם...

...from the fruit of her hand,
she plants a vineyard.

*A*nd she made a vow and said, "Lord of
Hosts, if You will indeed look upon the
affliction of Your handmaid...and give Your
handmaid a man child, then I will give him to
Hashem all the days of his life...."

(I Shmuel 1:11)

The First of Her Fruits

A sliver of moon shone down on the caravan winding its way into town. From astride his donkey, Elkanah peered ahead into the darkness. Where would he be able to camp for the night? Where was there enough space for his large family: his two wives, Chanah and Peninah, and Peninah's many children?

Elkanah led the caravan and Chanah followed behind, holding one of Peninah's younger daughters close to her in the saddle. Then came Peninah, with two babies in her arms, and seven donkeys driven by her older sons. The rest of the beasts plodded along after them, laden with sacks of bread and salty cheese, large flasks of wine and water, piles of blankets and folded tents. But there was no doubt in anyone's mind which provisions were the most important: the baskets and baskets of dates, figs, pomegranates, and olives—the first of Elkanah's produce.

"Auntie Chanah," asked the little girl in Chanah's lap, "why did we pack so much fruit? Do we have to eat it all when we get to Shiloh?"

Chanah smiled and hugged her tightly. "This fruit is not for us to eat," she explained. "It is a gift for the priests in the Tabernacle."

"Why do we need to bring them a gift?"

Chanah shifted in the saddle and smoothed the little girl's hair. "It is easy to think of God in times of trouble," she explained. "What if there were a drought, God forbid, and the trees dried up? Or heavy rains washed away our crops? Then we would all call out to Him. But what happens when we have what we need? We may feel that it was our own strength and wisdom that brought us all our blessings. Since we planted the seeds and watered them, we may feel that *we* really caused them to grow. We may forget that without God nothing could exist. So every year we bring our first fruits to the Tabernacle to show God that we remember Him even in times of plenty."

The child looked around as they rode through the town. The streets were empty. In one home after another, families gathered for their evening meal.

"So why aren't all the townspeople going up to Shiloh, too?" she asked. "Don't they know that Shavuot is coming?"

"They do, darling," Chanah said, "but they don't realize how important it is to go to Shiloh."

The little girl opened her eyes wide. "There must be a way to get people to come," she insisted.

"There is only one way to make a real change in the world," explained Chanah as she nodded toward the long caravan behind them. "First you must correct your own deeds. Then you can influence your family, your friends, and your neighbors. After that, others in your city will learn from you and slowly your message will spread out to the entire nation."

"Like Abba does!" cried the little girl in sudden comprehension.

Chanah squeezed her small frame closer. "That's right," she said. "Your father takes us up to Shiloh three times a year. But he doesn't just take the shortest route. Every time, he travels by way of different towns. And every time, new people see him and ask where he's heading. And many of them join him. More and more people are going up to the Tabernacle every year just because of his example."

By now they had reached the center of town. The large square was deserted. As always, the family did not look for lodgings. Elkanah and the older children set up tents out in the street and gathered wood for a fire. Peninah laid out blankets for her younger ones, and Chanah started to heat the family's supper. The girl clung to Chanah's side as she worked. She loved the patient woman who always had time for her questions.

"Where is my little one?" Peninah called as she neared the fire. "Where is my little girl? There you are! Come to your mother!"

Peninah looked over at Chanah. "I wish I could help you with the cooking," she apologized as she scooped up her daughter, "but I must put my young ones to bed. And anyway, you're not busy with children...."

Chanah tightened her grip on the pot in her hands. How could Peninah be so cruel, especially when they were on their way to the Tabernacle? Why did she have to mar the most joyous events by her taunts? Chanah could not understand it. Peninah was usually thoughtful, but whenever they traveled to Shiloh she seemed to have no sympathy.

The family was up early the next morning, folding blankets and strapping tents onto their donkeys' backs. Despite the hour, the square was already filling with curious onlookers wondering who these strange campers were. Elkanah went from one person to another, telling of their destination and urging all to come along.

"We are on our way to the Lord's house in Shiloh!" he repeated to each new spectator. "The Tabernacle still stands there, as it has stood since the days of Yehoshua. Scholars are gathering to teach and judge disputes. The priests are preparing to offer your sacrifices. Do not stay away any longer. Pack up and join us! Bring your children and show them how a festival is celebrated!"

As Elkanah spoke, the old men remembered the days of their youth and tears streamed down their wrinkled cheeks. Children tugged at their fathers' hands, begging to take part in the journey. And women began to feel they could wait no longer to open their hearts in prayer at this holy site. Soon one family after another was packing up to join the caravan.

Elkanah made his way through the crowded Tabernacle courtyard with portions of roasted meat from his peace offering. After much searching, his family had found a quiet spot where they could enjoy the festive meal. Chanah's eyes met her husband's and she saw that he was filled with joy.

"Look how many more people are here than there were last year!" he beamed.

"Yes," she nodded, "the nation is beginning to wake up. Thanks to you."

"And to my family," Elkanah added. "But you know, every Jew has that spark within him, that need to open his heart and pray. It just has to be aroused."

Chanah fought the feeling that rose within her. Perhaps not every Jew could pray, she thought. Sometimes it was too painful. How many times could she uncover the raw place within her that awaited a child? How many tears could she shed? Wasn't it better to let wounds heal than to rip them open time after time?

As the family assembled for the festive meal, Chanah took the seat that Elkanah had saved by his side. As always, he carved for her the choicest piece of meat. He never let her forget that she was the wife of his youth, the closest to his heart. He had married Peninah to raise a family, but he made certain that Chanah knew his love for her had never diminished.

"My husband loves me and prays for me," she reasoned. "If his prayers have not been accepted, what more can I do?"

Peninah's loud voice broke into her thoughts. "Please give some more to our oldest son," she asked

Elkanah. "And to this son, too.... And to our daughters...."

She looked over at Chanah's plate and her eyes widened in astonishment. "I really don't see why you need such a large portion," she said, "since you have no one to share it with...."

Chanah turned white. What was wrong with this woman? Had she no mercy at all? She could not hold back the tears that burned in her eyes. All the hidden embers of pain within her now burst forth, searing her heart. She dropped her fork and turned away from the family, wishing she could escape forever.

Elkanah bent close and whispered with sudden fury, "Don't listen to her. And don't let her make you cry. You have my love, which is greater than even the love ten sons could give you."

But Chanah did not answer. Although she heard his words, she did not feel their comfort. Suddenly she understood that no matter how much her husband loved her, his love could not replace the love of a child. And no matter how he prayed, his prayers could not replace her own.

She fled from the table and pushed her way through the crowd, heading towards the hall where the altar stood. Eli, the high priest, sat at the entrance.

Had Chanah looked back, she would have been surprised to see tears in Peninah's eyes as well, and pain etched in her face. If Chanah had turned back, she may have begun to understand the motive behind Peninah's stinging words.

"Chanah prays for a child," thought Peninah, "yet perhaps she does not pray with all her heart. She tries to run from her pain, not to face it. But that defeats God's purpose in giving her this test. Just as He withheld children from Sarah, Rivkah, and Rachel in order to move them to prayer, so does He desire Chanah's deepest supplications. But Elkanah is always trying to comfort her. She must be pushed to cry out to Heaven, especially now, when we are in the Lord's house."

Peninah sighed and shook her head. "And I must help her..."

❦

Chanah found a place against the wall where she would not be jostled by the masses of people bringing their offerings. She closed her eyes and swayed in silence. Only her lips moved; her voice could not be heard.

"Lord of multitudes," she began as the roar of voices swirled around her, "of all the millions of souls You have created, have You not one left for me? At the banquet of a king, a single slice of bread is surely not a great request. Is it difficult for You, King of all life, to grant me just one child?

"You created me," she continued, "but I feel that I have no permanence in Your world. Every creature has its own claim to the future. Angels have no children but they never die; they exist forever. Those of flesh and blood live only a short time, but they leave children in their place.

"And what am I?" Chanah cried out in her silence. "Just a fleeting shadow, neither angel nor mortal? Either let me live forever, or give me a child of my own!"

Chanah began to tremble as waves of grief washed over her. She pressed her arms to her chest and huddled closer to the wall.

"Did You create any part of my body without purpose?" she demanded. "My eyes see; my ears hear; I have hands for work and legs for walking. But why did You give me these breasts upon my heart if I have no infant to suckle?

"I do not ask for an exceptional child," she went on in desperation. "Better he not stand out as the wisest or the most handsome. Just grant me a normal child whom I can teach and inspire. Then I will dedicate him to Your service all the days of his life...."

Chanah did not notice that the hall had begun to clear. She hugged the wall, her lips moving soundlessly, unable to stem the flow of prayer she had finally let loose.

Suddenly she heard a rough voice. It seemed to be coming from far away, rousing her from her meditation. "How long will you stand here in your drunkenness? Come back when your wine has left you!"

Chanah slowly opened her eyes. Who would dare to come to this holy spot drunk? She looked up to see the high priest standing before her, studying her closely.

She gasped and the blood drained from her face. "No, sir," she protested. "I am a bitter woman who has had not a drop of wine. I am here to pour out my soul before the Lord. Do not consider me so brazen as to come here inebriated. It is only due to my great distress that I have spoken until now."

Eli lowered his eyes. "Go in peace," he calmed her.

"May the God of Israel grant whatever request you have asked of Him."

"May your servant find favor," whispered Chanah as she backed out of the sanctuary.

❦

Chanah held fast to the reins of her donkey as she once again made her way up to Shiloh. Again the caravan wound through the hillside. Again their tents and blankets were piled high on the backs of their many beasts. And again she held a child tightly beside her in the saddle. But this time the child was her own.

On previous journeys they had brought the first fruits of their field; now she brought the first fruit of her womb. She remembered the words she'd said, although it seemed so long ago: "It is easy to think of God in times of trouble. But do we remember Him even in times of plenty?"

The young boy leaned back sleepily against her breast. "When will we get there, Mama? When will we see all the animals, and the people, and Eli, the old man you told me about?"

"You will see soon enough, little one," Chanah whispered as she watched him fight to stay awake. "Soon enough you will see where I prayed for you."

"Where you made the promise?"

"Yes, Shmuel," she nodded as the words echoed in her mind: "Grant me a child and I will dedicate him to Your service all the days of his life...."

"And I will stay there?"

Chanah looked out at the mountain ridge on the

far horizon. Shiloh wasn't much farther now. She passed a hand over her son's thick hair. "It will be your new home, Shmuel. And your father and I shall visit you often. And Eli will take good care of you. And he will teach you many things...."

"And will I be one of the priests?"

"No, honey," Chanah smiled. "You are a Levite. You will *help* the priests. And you will learn a lot of Torah."

"Like the stories Papa tells me?"

"Yes. And much, much more."

"I won't be alone, right Mama? God will be close to me there?"

"Closer than you can imagine," whispered Chanah.

I Shmuel 1
MeAm Loez
Yalkut Shimoni
Berachot 31a

כפה פרשה לעני.....

She spreads out her
palm to the poor....

*T*he highest form of charity is to strengthen the hand of a poor Jew with a gift, or a loan, or by taking him in as a partner...so that he will not feel the need to ask [for charity].

[The third-highest form of charity] is when the benefactor knows to whom he is giving but the poor person does not know from whom he is taking. Thus we find that the great sages would secretly leave money in the doorways of the poor. And it is proper to act this way.

(Maimonides, *Mishneh Torah*, Gifts to the Poor 10:7, 9)

Charity Begins at Home

"A little garlic would be just right," thought Mar Ukva's wife as she lifted a spoonful of stew from the large, enamel pot and put it to her lips. Then she turned and called out to her friend cutting salad in the dining room, "The guests will be coming soon. With your help we'll be ready just in time!"

The front door burst open without warning. The first guest of the afternoon strode in and scowled in the direction of the dining room.

"You're sitting in my seat!" he shouted.

The woman at the table raised her head in shock. Mar Ukva's wife turned towards the voice and hurried out of the kitchen. She hoped to hold her friend back from an impending argument, but she was too late.

"I'm sitting in your seat, am I?" the friend challenged. "And who are you, anyway? Is this your house?"

"It's not my house, but it's my seat," he insisted. "I sit here every afternoon, and I'm not about to change today."

"Now, now," Mar Ukva's wife tried to calm him as she placed a steaming plate on the table. "Here's your dinner. Relax and enjoy it."

"It's about time you served me," the old man grumbled. "I haven't had a bite to eat all day, and your friend here takes my seat, and you dawdle with my food...."

"Come help me in the kitchen," Mar Ukva's wife whispered to her friend as the old man kept up a steady stream of complaints.

"Of all the nerve!" fumed her friend as soon as she had closed the kitchen door behind her. "How do you let a guest in your home speak to you like that? And to your friends! Why, he's nothing but a beggar!"

Mar Ukva's wife nodded. "I know, but you must understand that he's been coming here for an early dinner every afternoon for the past fifteen years. And he always sits in the same place. In his mind, that chair rightfully belongs to him."

"But the way he snapped at you when you served him! Why do you put up with that?"

"It's certainly more pleasant to serve a guest who smiles and says 'thank you'—I won't argue with that. But should I let him starve just because he's rude?"

Her friend shook her head in confusion. "I don't know..." she said. "It just might serve him right."

"Look at it this way," said Mar Ukva's wife. "The

Almighty has cared for my needs, and He in turn commands me to care for the needs of those less fortunate. Does it make any difference if some of my guests fail to appreciate what I do for them?"

❦

Hours later she brushed the last crumbs off the table. "Well, business was good today," she thought. Every last bit of stew was finished, and only a few small rolls remained in the breadbasket. Was it the cold weather that had made them hungrier than usual, or had there been that many new faces among the familiar crowd?

Luckily, she had put aside some food for Mar Ukva; otherwise, he would have had no dinner at all to come home to. "After feeding everybody else, could I let my own husband go hungry? After all, charity begins at home," she reminded herself.

As a matter of fact, where was he?

She looked out at the darkened sky. He would be home any time now. "I'll go meet him outside the study hall. He is probably lecturing later than usual."

Wrapping her cape around her shoulders, Mar Ukva's wife made her way up the dirt path to the top of the hill. As she rounded a corner, the study hall came into view. The large hall would soon begin to empty out as men of all ages headed home for their evening meal. Mar Ukva's wife knew that her husband, the head of the academy, would be the last to emerge.

But what was this? Reb Abba, one of the most respected sages in the city, was hurrying down the steps of the study hall!

Mar Ukva's wife watched in astonishment from across the road. Was the sage so eager to finish learning?

Reb Abba continued to act strangely. At the bottom of the steps he stopped, hoisted a large sack over his shoulder, and took a seat on a rock shadowed by the building. His back to the main path, he bent over a book and lost himself in study.

Now Mar Ukva's wife began to see the purpose of the sage's swift exit. As the first students filed out, the poorer ones passed behind him and reached into the cloth slung over his back. Only she noticed who extracted a few coins to feed his family that day. No one else saw; not even Reb Abba. When his heavy sack became light, he knew that all the money was gone and he continued on his way. He would never know who had benefited from his charity.

"Our town is so full of kindness," thought Mar Ukva's wife as she watched Reb Abba from afar. And was it any wonder? Wasn't every Jew descended from Avraham? Hadn't they all inherited his mercy, humility, and kindness?

Her husband also distributed charity on his way home from the study hall. But instead of the needy coming to him, he would go to the needy. Every evening he passed certain homes and placed a handful of coins between the door hinges. Before the holidays, he gave out extra.

She thought back to the Yom Kippur that had recently passed....

❧

Mar Ukva had been about to step out the door, pockets full of silver, when an urgent matter was brought to his attention.

"I must go take care of this right away!" he cried. "But what will I do about the poor families? They are waiting for the money so they can buy food to eat before the fast begins. Can I let them down now?"

"Why are you so worried?" his wife asked him. "Isn't our son old enough to make your rounds today? Tell him the names and amounts, and trust him to distribute the money."

Mar Ukva looked over at the boy uncertainly.

"It's a good way to educate him," his wife added.

Calling to his son, Mar Ukva explained the task. "Remember, people are depending on this money. Since I have been giving it to them faithfully, year after year, it is no longer merely an act of goodwill. It has become an obligation."

The boy opened his eyes wide and listened solemnly to his father's words. But good intentions are not always enough, and a child's decisions will often differ from those of his father.

Hours later the boy returned, his sack empty but for one small purse of coins.

"Whom was this meant for?" asked Mar Ukva.

"For the poor water carrier who lives at the edge of the city," said the child. "But he doesn't need it."

"How do you know?" asked his father sternly, already regretting that he had entrusted such an important task to a mere boy.

"I passed by the window and saw the water carrier sitting at his table. His son was pouring him a cup of very old wine from a large decanter. I could smell it outside," the child concluded definitively.

His mother waited for Mar Ukva to respond. Would he be angered at the water carrier for feigning poverty all these years? Would he curse him for spending charity money on fine wine?

Finally, her husband slapped his hand on the table in frustration. "If only I had known," he said after a few minutes. "If only someone had told me....

"Anyone who has acquired a taste for old wine has lived a life of luxury. The water carrier must have been raised in a wealthy home, and used to the best food and drink. How difficult must it be for him now that he has fallen on hard times. How he must miss the pleasures he was once accustomed to, especially on holidays!"

He dug his hand deep into his pocket.

"Quick!" he called to the boy. "There is hardly time left to shop and cook before the festive meal. Take these coins, add them to the purse, and run to the water carrier's home. He must get twice as much money as I used to send him!"

Mar Ukva's wife smiled to herself as she thought of her husband. Although he regularly gave much of his wealth to the poor, he did not consider himself particularly generous. The money God granted him was not his own, he reasoned. It was merely his responsibility to distribute it to its rightful owners.

There he was now, coming down the steps.

"What a pleasure!" declared Mar Ukva as he caught

sight of his wife. "I was hoping you might come."

"I thought to join you on your rounds tonight so I could see you sooner."

The night wind refreshed them as they walked. "How the town has grown!" she exclaimed. "Look how far the new houses have reached!"

"Students are joining the academy all the time," commented Mar Ukva. "They are moving here with their families from all over the Land of Israel. Some have come from as far away as Babylonia."

"Just look at all the homes where the wheat field used to be," his wife marveled.

"Yes," sighed Mar Ukva. "They all wish to learn and to support their families. But it is hard to find work...."

Mar Ukva's wife interrupted him. "Let the Creator worry about the needs of His creatures," she chided. "Does anyone ever go hungry in this city?"

Down one street and up another, Mar Ukva was familiar with each home. At this one he would nod a greeting and pass quickly by. At the next he would pause and bend to leave a coin or two in the door. At one home he added a piece of silver, for he had heard of a baby born there. At another he stopped to whisper a prayer, for that evening he had noticed that the scholar who lived there looked worried.

The city spread before him in the dark as if it were his great Talmudic academy. Each candlelit home was like a student; each with its own face, its own needs....

Just as he began turning in to one of the houses, the door opened and a man came rushing towards them.

"I must see who leaves me money every night!" he called out. "Wait! Wait! Let me thank you!"

Mar Ukva and his wife dashed off ahead, but the man ran after them.

"You must not let him discover your identity!" Mar Ukva's wife cried as they raced ahead. "He would be very embarrassed to know it's you, the head of the academy, who takes the trouble to leave him money every night. He might not even want you to know he's so poor."

Weary from a day's work, Mar Ukva's wife had little strength left to run, and she knew they could not elude their pursuer much longer. Up ahead, she saw the baker's large, brick oven.

"Come!" she panted. "Follow me!" She raced over to the large oven and climbed inside.

"Quick!" she urged as Mar Ukva climbed in after her. The small, brick room was black with soot, and in the moonlight streaking in through the chimney they saw swirls of smoke still rising off the oven bottom. The baker must have just taken out his coals, for the earthen floor retained its heat.

Mar Ukva began to jump painfully from one foot to the other. "I don't know how much longer I can stand here!" he gasped as he looked over at his wife.

"Oh, look at your poor feet!" she cried. "Here, stand on top of mine."

Only then did he notice that his wife was standing perfectly still. The heat did not seem to bother her. Her feet were not scorched one bit.

Mar Ukva rested his feet on hers and leaned weakly against the wall. "What merit does my wife have that

I don't?" he thought dejectedly. "What is my sin that I am unworthy of such a miracle?"

"Don't worry," his wife reassured him when she saw his despair. "There are eight levels of charity and you have reached one of the highest. You are busy teaching Torah, yet you take the time to go from house to house every night. You could give out the money much more easily right in the study hall, but you wish to remain anonymous. There is nothing lacking in your deeds."

She looked down at her unsinged shoes. Her thoughts returned to the crotchety old man and the dozens of other hungry folk who'd passed through her door that afternoon.

"The only reason my merit is greater is that I bring the poor right into our home and serve them at our table. They do not need to shop and cook. Their benefit is immediate."

Later that night, Mar Ukva's wife had time to think further. There is much reward to be received even for giving charity reluctantly, or for giving less than expected, or for giving after being asked. Far better is to give pleasantly, before one is asked, and better yet is to protect the dignity of the poor by giving as Reb Abba does, without ever seeing who benefits from one's money. "But my husband's deeds are greater still because he conceals his identity while helping others," she mused.

"Today, however, God has shown me that my humble form of charity is the most meritorious of all. By welcoming the poor into my home, as if they were members of my own family, I do more than hand them money. I become involved with them as people, comforting them in times of trouble, sharing their joys, and sometimes even suffering the abuse and ingratitude of bitter souls."

No one can measure the amount of kindness that kept Mar Ukva's wife at a hot stove day after day and year after year. No one, that is, but the Heavenly Judge, who paid her back in kind as she stood unharmed in the heat of that burning oven.

Ketubot 67b and *Ein Yaakov* ad loc.
Maimonides, *Mishneh Torah*, Gifts to the
    Poor 10:7, 9
Rabbi Chaim Shmuelevitz, *Sichot Mussar*,
    part 2, essay 34

...שש וארגמן לבושה.

...fine linen and purple
are her clothing.

*M*y soul is far removed from peace...."
Rabbi Abba says, ["peace" refers to]
a made bed, and a wife who beautifies
herself for her scholarly husband.

(Shabbat 25b)

When [Abba Chilkiyah] came to the city, his
wife came out to greet him bedecked with
jewelry.

(Taanit 23b)

Along with the Manna

*L*et them laugh," sighed the wife of Abba Chilkiyah as she passed the women returning from the marketplace.

Looking back over her shoulder, she could see them whispering to one another. She didn't need to hear their words to know what they were saying:

"Look at her! Is she off to a wedding?"

"How does she get her housework done if she's primping all day?"

"The way she carries on, you'd never know she's the wife of a holy man!"

Indeed, there was no disputing that her husband was a holy man. After all, he was the grandson of Choni HaMe'agel, the great sage who drew a circle around his feet in times of drought and vowed not to budge until the heavens opened up. Furthermore, Abba Chilkiyah was a miracle worker in his own right, often interceding for his fellow Jews.

The rain that always fell as a result of Abba Chilkiyah's prayers was proof of his virtue, but what of his wife? Why did she adorn herself every afternoon? When all the other women were home with their families, why did she head towards the edge of town wearing her finest clothes?

The women slowly made their way down the cobblestone road. The sacks of flour balanced on their shoulders and the vegetable baskets cradled in their arms were not as full as in previous seasons. Fresh produce was increasingly hard to find for it had been a long summer. The rains had not fallen as usual after the Sukkot festival, and now, as Chanukah approached, all of Israel was praying for relief.

"We feel the drought more than anyone," sighed one woman as she shifted her package from one hip to the other.

"Of course we do," agreed a friend. "Once the children have some food in their stomachs, they run outdoors to play. But we immediately have to search for something to cook for the next meal."

"And what about our husbands?" sniffed a third. "How can they sit all evening and concentrate on their learning with their families so hungry?"

"Oh, why begrudge them those hours of study," one of the others said softly. "Don't they work hard enough? I'm happy to let my husband learn at the end of a long, hot day. I only wish I could do more to lift his spirits."

Everyone hurried to reassure her: "You shop, you bake, you clean the house. What more can a woman do?"

❦

Abba Chilkiyah's wife bent over her mirror. It had been a stressful week, and her face showed it. Too many late nights and early mornings, too much heat and too much worry. Was it always this bad every time there was a drought, with so many people ill and needing assistance? She could not remember.

She could barely recall what a normal summer was like: cisterns brimming with cool, clear water; children filling tubs for play.... What had she done with her time when she hadn't been rushing from one house to another to feed the sick? Surely she had always found plenty of things to do, but right now she could not remember a single one.

"I look as exhausted as I feel," she admitted as she blended the colorful powders in her tray, "but I won't let it show. Especially not to my husband.

"Thank Heaven for Ezra's wisdom!" thought Abba Chilkiyah's wife as she dabbed fragrance behind her ear.

Even now, when many stalls in the marketplace were boarded up for lack of goods, the perfume vendor still made his rounds. Ezra had passed a law centuries earlier requiring cosmetics peddlers to frequent even the most distant villages.

"He was a great leader," she marveled, "yet he was

concerned with the needs of the women."

She remembered how her mother had told her about the manna when she was a girl. "Do you think that when we were wandering in the desert, all God sent us was food?" her mother asked. "Jewelry also fell along with the manna, and sweet-smelling powders."

"But Mother," she protested, "weren't we struggling for our very lives in the wilderness? Why should God have performed miracles just so the women could be beautiful? Are looks as important as the bread we eat? Besides, isn't what's within a person the thing that matters most?"

Her mother smiled. "A beautiful wife is very important, especially to a Torah scholar."

"A Torah scholar, Mother? Holy men don't notice things like that!"

"One day, my daughter, you'll understand," was all her mother said.

She dressed herself in silk, wrapped a brightly painted shawl around her shoulders, and headed towards the wheat fields.

The sky was barren; clear and unyielding.

"If a drop of rain were to fall right now," she thought, "it would be like manna from heaven."

Abba Chilkiyah's wife reached the edge of town and scanned the horizon. A sudden gust of wind whipped the beaded fringes of her shawl against her cheek. Soon she recognized her husband's form trudging through the parched field. But today he was not alone. Who were the men at his side?

Abba Chilkiyah walked towards her. His face was

red from hours in the sun and his beard was powdered with dust. But as he gazed at his wife, a smile transformed his features.

"You must realize that your husband is a great and holy man," her mother had told her soon after her marriage. "And the greater the man, the greater his temptations. A Torah scholar is never oblivious to the beauty of this world. In fact, he is more sensitive than others."

Her mother had paused and considered her next words carefully. "Your husband's soul has been put in your trust. Make sure it never grows restless. Make sure that in his eyes, you are always the most beautiful."

As they walked home, the townswomen gawked. But Abba Chilkiyah took no notice. From the moment he had seen his wife at the field's edge, his weariness had lifted. Now, walking beside her, his eyes did not wander from her for an instant.

The men who had accompanied them home sat quietly as Abba Chilkiyah finished his supper.

"Excuse us for a moment," he said to them as he rose from the table.

"I know why these sages met me in the field," he whispered as his wife followed him outside. "Before they ask me to pray for rain, let's go quietly up to the rooftop and beg for God's mercy. This way, our intervention will go unnoticed."

Together they climbed to the roof. Abba Chilkiyah stood in one corner and his wife in another. They closed their eyes tightly and prayed for a blessing upon the land.

As they opened their eyes, they saw storm clouds overhead.

"Thank God!" cried Abba Chilkiyah when they returned to the waiting men. "It seems you have no need for me after all."

"You haven't fooled us," replied the sages. "We know why you went outside. We saw the clouds gather as you both stood on the rooftop. The rain has only come because of you."

Rain spilled over the domed houses and left clean streaks on their dusty, stone walls. Rivers of water began to swell and course through the narrow roads. The village women shouted in joy and ran out to fill their buckets.

Abba Chilkiyah's wife listened to their laughter as she stood at her doorway. She was smiling now, too, but for a different reason. "The honor of God lies in hidden things..." she thought to herself, recalling King Solomon's words. "My merit is also hidden. The village women may never understand me, but in heaven there is a true Judge."

Only Abba Chilkiyah, on the opposite side of the rooftop, and the sages watching from below had witnessed the power of one woman's prayer. They alone knew her secret. For when a distant rumble had broken the stillness, and the thunderclouds had gathered overhead, they had risen first in her direction.

Taanit 23a-b
Shabbat 25b and *Iyun Yaakov* ad loc.
Yoma 75a

עוז והדר לבושה....

Strength and majesty
are her raiment....

*W*omen are obligated to kindle the
Chanukah lights for they, too,
were included in the miracle.

(Shabbat 23a)

...the miracle occurred by virtue of...Yehudit.

(Tosafot, Pesachim 105b)

*It is customary for women to refrain from work
while the candles are burning...because another
miracle happened then by virtue of a woman.*

(MeAm Loez, Bemidbar, p. 98)

From Between the Jaws

*Y*ehudit put down her sewing to answer another knock at the door. "Please," begged a woman, "give me anything, even some coarse flour or a few beans. I cannot just sit by and watch my children die."

Yehudit turned away from her and wept. She was as hungry as everyone else, but her neighbors refused to believe it. How could these desperate souls understand? In the past she had always been there to help, opening her home to anyone in need. But now she had nothing to offer.

She reached deep into her cloak and produced a handful of gold pieces. The woman fingered the coins instinctively and then let them fall back into Yehudit's palm. If there was no food left to buy in all of Jerusalem, what good was gold? Could it nourish her children?

That night Yehudit lay awake. In the silence, she thought back to the start of the siege....

❦

"Fellow Jews! Fellow Jews!" called a messenger as he ran through the city streets. "Come to the Temple courtyard! Pray for your lives!"

A tremor of fear moving through her body, Yehudit hurried towards the Temple. The streets surged with confusion as more and more people poured out of their homes. A large group clustered around one man who seemed to know what was happening. As she drew near, Yehudit heard:

"...and then today, at about noon, a foreign nobleman was found at the city gates lying on the ground in chains. He said that the Greek general Heliphornes had abandoned him there because he'd spoken up for the Jews.

"You see, he had been captured in one of Heliphornes's recent battles, and had overheard him planning to attack Jerusalem. 'No, my master,' he had tried to warn him. 'You are making a mistake. Their God may grant you victory in order to chastise His people, but your triumph will only herald your downfall. Look at Pharaoh and Nebuchadnezzer. What remains of their glorious empires? And yet the small Jewish nation survives....'

"Heliphornes heard the captive's words and flew into a rage. 'No people in the world has stood up to me, yet you dare to speak in favor of this miserable nation?'

"With that, he ordered the nobleman bound in chains.

"'I shall conquer Jerusalem!' he declared. 'And you will be among the Jews when I slaughter them!'"

A murmur passed through the crowd, and the man paused before continuing.

"This good nobleman has warned us of the Greeks' plans. He says that at this very moment, thousands of horsemen and infantry are encamped in the valley below the city walls."

So this was the reason for the urgent call to prayer!

The Jews posted sentries around the walls and archers on the hills to lie in wait for the Greeks.

But Heliphornes found the city's water source outside the walls and commanded his men to shatter the pipes that ran from it. "Why should I lose men in battle?" he thought shrewdly. "The summer has just begun and we can be comfortable in this valley for some time. I will simply station my troops around the walls so that no one can bring in food or water. With a bit of patience, Jerusalem will be mine!"

Yehudit sighed as she recalled the slow but relentless progress of the siege. Within a few months, food supplies had dwindled and cisterns had run dry.

Her wealth could no longer help the people, yet she felt duty-bound to ease their suffering. A plan began to form in her mind, and as crazy as it was, she knew there was no turning back. She was convinced that her late husband would have approved. Certainly he would have agreed that doing something, anything—even the most reckless act—was better than helplessly awaiting the end.

The next morning, Yehudit hurried out to speak with the commanders of the Jewish army. As she neared their headquarters, she heard mobs demanding surrender.

"Let's go out to them!"

"We'll give ourselves up!"

"Better to be captives than to die of hunger!"

Yehudit shuddered and pushed her way through the crowd. Was it really better? she wondered. What would they do with those too young or too old for hard labor? And what would become of the women in the hands of those animals?

Cutting through the shouting throngs, she suddenly found herself standing before Uziahu, the general of the city's army.

"Let us wait five more days," he was saying. "If our prayers aren't answered in the next five days, then we'll surrender."

As the crowd began to disperse, the general's gaze fell upon Yehudit. "Ah, here is the beautiful daughter of Beeri, the proud and independent widow," he thought bitterly. "So she, too, has come to plead for surrender? What has become of our people?"

But then he saw Yehudit step forward. She was not as pale as those around her, and she did not have the same panic in her eyes.

"My master," she said softly, "I wish to speak with you and your officers in private."

The men shook their heads in disbelief as they listened to Yehudit's scheme.

"I will go tonight," she concluded. "All I ask is that your soldiers let me exit through the city gate without asking me any questions."

Uziahu looked over at his officers and raised his palms in despair. "Do we have a choice?" he sighed. "We will wait for news of your return."

Silently, he wondered if they would ever see her again....

❧

Her hand trembled as she pulled the dress out from the back of her closet. How long had it been since she had worn it? She loved this dress, with its deep purple satin. A splash of wine. A splash of blood.

Jerusalem was no longer the place to wear such a dress. If she climbed between thornbushes in search of wild herbs to cook, its long hem would catch at her feet. If she helped her servants haul home pails of precious water, its snug sleeves would strain in protest. And how could she remind her neighbors of her former wealth as they watched their loved ones slowly giving way to thirst and hunger?

That was one form of suffering she would not have to endure, she sighed as she slipped the dress off its hanger. For once, she took comfort in the fact that her husband had passed away before the onset of the seige.

He would have understood her now. He always had. While some had been appalled by her independence, he had delighted in it.

She brushed her thick, black hair and studied herself in the mirror. What would the Greek general think of her? Surely he had taken for himself the most beautiful women in every country he'd invaded. They probably filled his harem at this very moment, awaiting his return.

But as she put on her ruby earrings and twisted a ruby-studded turban around her head, Yehudit knew that she was more than beautiful. She was regal.

Her thoughts were interrupted by a knock at the door.

"The basket is ready, my lady!" cried a servant.

"Is it elegantly arranged?" she questioned the young girl. "After all, it's for a general. Did they put in everything I asked for? Bread? Salty cheese? Oh, and the wine.... The wine is very important!"

"Yes, yes," the girl nodded. "They weren't easy to find in this city, but we finally gathered everything you requested."

Yehudit hurried downstairs to the kitchen. As she passed the window, she was struck by the eerie silence in the streets. It was only early evening. Where were all the people? Where were all the children shouting as they chased each other through the courtyards?

She took her basket and slipped out of the house. Most of the homes she passed were sunk in darkness, their inhabitants seeking relief from their hunger in exhausted sleep. But Yehudit had no problem staying awake. She beheld the city wall looming before her. Soon she would be leaving the safety of its confines. But did it create a shelter or a prison? Enemies without; hunger within....

As she approached to the city gate, she saw that Uziahu had joined the soldiers guarding the wall.

"May God protect you," he whispered, "as you go among the enemy."

Yehudit began climbing down the mountain. Peril surrounded her, pricking her skin like a thousand tiny arrows. She was alert to every sound, every movement. Fires crackled in the valley below and Greek soldiers huddled around them. Their words drifted through the night:

"Wish we could just go in and crush them already...."

"...get home before winter...."

"How long can we camp here with nothing to do?"

Yehudit stepped carefully, trying not to snap any branches or send loose rocks rolling down the slope. They would discover her soon enough, but right now she needed a few more minutes to review her story.

Would Heliphornes suspect? Would he trust her? Everything depended on that.

She quickened her steps. They heard her now. There was no turning back.

"Who's there?" shouted a soldier. "Identify yourself!"

"I am a Hebrew woman," answered Yehudit from the darkness. "I have escaped from the city. Let me speak...."

"Come forward! Let us see you!" they commanded.

Yehudit stepped into the firelight.

"Who would have thought that the Jews have such beautiful maidens," remarked their leader.

"I know that Jerusalem is about to fall into your hands," she said breathlessly. "I would rather be on your side. Take me to Heliphornes and I will show him how to enter the city without losing any men."

The leader stood up and addressed her gruffly. "Very well, come with us. The general will be quite pleased with our find...."

It was early morning when Yehudit was ushered into the large tent that served as Heliphornes' reception room. The general sat propped up on his couch, a velvet robe straining at his ample girth. As he gazed open-mouthed at her, she forced her head down modestly lest he glimpse the loathing in her eyes.

"Have no fear," he grinned, leaning forward in his seat. "I will not harm anyone who wishes to serve me, especially not a servant as pleasing as you are. Now tell me why you have come."

"My people have sinned before the Lord," explained Yehudit. "That is why God has sent you against them. Yet even now they do not repent; they only add to their sins."

Heliphornes had heard of this God before. Hadn't that impudent nobleman threatened him with God's revenge? But now it seemed that God had sent him here; that they were working as partners to punish Israel for its sins!

He looked at Yehudit in amusement. "What sins are you speaking of, my daughter?"

"Well, their past sins are too numerous to mention," she said quickly. "But now, starvation is making them rebel even more. They are talking about slaughtering the beasts that were set aside for the Temple service, and distributing the meat among the people.

"God will not stand by their side anymore. He has appeared to me in a vision and instructed me to aid you in battle. I can lead you through the secret passageways of the city."

Heliphornes studied her impassively.

Did he trust her? She could not be sure.

"I have come here to serve you," she insisted, "and to bring you the word of my God. I must leave the camp three times a day to pray to Him in solitude. Only then will He tell me exactly when He plans to punish the Jews. And then I can lead you to victory!"

Heliphornes looked at Yehudit with satisfaction. What harm could there be in keeping her around?

"You speak well," he nodded. "You will be safe with me." The king turned to his servants. "We will have a new guest at our table. Set a place next to mine."

Yehudit was prepared for this.

"My master," she excused herself, "I'm afraid I cannot accept this honor. You know that the Hebrews eat special foods. If I do not keep these laws, God may reject me. Then I will be of no help to you in your battle. I would be honored to sit with you, but I must eat only food I have brought with me."

"But you couldn't have brought enough food for more than a few days," Heliphornes protested. "What will you do when your supplies run out?"

Yehudit thought of Uziahu's promise to his starving people: five days and he would surrender. And she had used up one already....

"Take my word, my master," she smiled. "It will not be more than a few days before God has His revenge."

These words pleased Heliphornes immensely. Not only would this woman expose the city's weak points—making the battle all but won—but she was even promising victory within days. That meant an end to this tedious siege, with the sun scorching their tents and nary a breeze for nights on end. As far as Heliphornes was concerned, his return home could not come soon enough....

Yehudit looked around her tent. A bed, a chair, a washbasin. It was an army camp, after all. She sat on the edge of her bed and tried to focus her mind. She had gotten this far, but what lay ahead? Here she was in the enemy's compound, free to come and go. Now all she had to do was to get the general alone.

She shivered and suddenly felt alarmed. What was she doing here? All her life had been spent in the safety of her home. She had never been alone with any man but her husband. And now she was deep inside the Greek camp, surrounded by thousands of coarse mercenaries.

She closed her eyes against the visions that rose in her mind. She had devised the best strategy she could, but who knew what would actually happen when she found herself alone with this idolator?

Yehudit remembered the words of the Shema: "And you shall love the Lord your God with all your heart, with all your soul, and with all your might."

She had always put her heart into helping God's nation; she had given of her might by generously sharing her wealth; and now she had a chance to offer her very soul, to risk her life in both this world and the next in order to save her people. Now she would put her very being in God's hands....

❧

Three uneventful days had passed since Yehudit entered the Greek encampment. That meant four days since Uziahu had promised to surrender. To-morrow the people would give themselves up. Her time was running out.

A servant came to her room, as if summoned by her thoughts. "The general requests that you join him for dinner," he announced, "in his private chambers."

Yehudit followed the servant through the maze of tents until they stood before that of Heliphornes. She swallowed hard, fighting the revulsion that seized her.

"Enter, enter," Heliphornes declared merrily as he lifted the tent flap to let her in. "You look so lovely tonight. Sit here beside me and eat your food."

"Isn't the general going to join me for dinner?" asked Yehudit as she lowered herself to a cushion.

"I would rather just sit and gaze at you. That alone is enough to satisfy my hunger."

Yehudit opened her basket and took out bread and cheese.

"It's so strange to eat alone," she said as a frown clouded her delicate features. "If you would share something with me, it would be much nicer."

Heliphornes smiled at her indulgently.

"Anything to put a smile back on your pretty face," he said, taking a slice of cheese.

Huge hunks of bread, lots of salty cheese.... She plied him with one thing after another until he was very thirsty. Yehudit poured them both some wine. And then more wine. And then more.

Before long the corpulent Greek was sprawled out on his bed, snoring loudly.

Yehudit wasted no time. Taking his sword in one hand and grasping his hair in the other, she pulled back his head and severed his neck with two clean blows. A stream of blood gushed forth, staining the bed. Yehudit twisted the length of hair in her hand and lifted his huge head. She placed it on the towels in her basket and quietly left the tent.

The camp guards nodded cordially as Yehudit passed through the gates. There was nothing unusual about her going out to the hills at this time for her evening prayers.

But tonight Yehudit went much farther than usual, climbing the mountain to her beleaguered city.

"Open the gates," she called out to the sentries at the city wall. "It is I, Yehudit."

Once again a messenger ran through the streets, leaving a trail of hastily lit windows in his wake.

"Up! Up! Everybody up!" he called out. "Grab your weapons and meet in the city square. Arise and prepare for battle!"

People began to congregate in the pre-dawn stillness. Bleary-eyed, their clothes thrown on at random, they strained to hear the sound of approaching troops, to glimpse their menacing forms in the distance.

The last thing they expected was to see the lovely widow Yehudit standing before them.

"Fellow Jews," she called out to the spellbound masses, "tomorrow you were to open the gates and give yourselves over to our oppressors." She motioned to the white flag already tied to a post in preparation for surrender.

"But the Almighty has guarded me in the midst of the enemy and I have returned to you in peace. There is no longer reason to despair."

With that, Yehudit opened her basket and pulled out the head of the Greek general. A stunned silence fell upon the crowd as she lifted it up for all to see. Then a roar rose from thousands of parched throats.

"Heliphornes is dead!"

"We are saved!"

"Thank God!"

Yehudit waited for the tumult to subside. Then she outlined the final phase of her plan.

"In less than an hour, the sun will rise and we shall hang the idolator's head on top of the wall, facing the Greek encampment. Then you shall gather your weapons and sound a war cry. But stay by the gates. Do not descend the mountain."

As Heliphornes' fleshy face dangled above them, the Hebrew army converged outside the city walls.

The first rays of day.... The piercing trumpet blasts....

Just as Yehudit had imagined, the guards rushed to their leader's tent the moment they heard the trumpets. He must be woken to instruct his troops. What did the Jews think they were doing? Would they really be foolhardy enough to attack the huge and powerful Greek army?

The blasts grew louder as they called through the flap of Heliphornes' tent. It seemed that no amount of noise could rouse him. From all over the camp, army officers rushed to the doorway. "Has the general been told?" they demanded.

The guards lowered their eyes in embarrassment. "We have been trying to wake him," they explained.

"There is no time!" cried the officers impatiently. "Why haven't you gone into his chambers?"

One guard turned red and whispered, "He is not alone. Our orders were not to disturb him."

"Oh, you know nothing of wartime!" snapped an exasperated officer as he pushed past the guards and hurried into the room. "Sir," he called out, "the enemy has taken up arms! The mice have crawled out of their holes!"

Hearing no sound behind the bed curtains, the officer pulled them apart to rouse their leader.

There lay Heliphornes' bloodied body, his neck an open gash, headless....

Screams of horror resounded through the encampment. "The Hebrew woman has killed Heliphornes!" they cried.

Thousands of terrified soldiers poured out of the camp. Looking up at the walls of Jerusalem, they saw their general's head hanging from the gate, overlooking masses of Hebrew soldiers. Without another look back, they fled to the hills.

The Jewish troops charged down the mountainside in close pursuit. The men who had been so beaten by the siege now felt the surge of energy that comes with impending victory. The mercenaries were rousted out of their hiding places, and their bodies strewn over the surrounding hills.

The Greek camp had been abandoned with more than enough supplies left behind to revive the starving people.

The jewels found in Heliphornes' chamber were not divided as spoils. The entire nation agreed that this wealth should go to the woman who had risked her life in that very place: the widow Yehudit.

But Yehudit had other plans for the treasure brought before her. All her life she had cared for the needs of her people. Now she would give this wealth to the Temple treasury, in order that the impoverished families might rebuild their lives.

As she watched the city coming back to life, Yehudit felt as if she, too, had merited resurrection. Going into the Greek camp, she had entered the very mouth of a lion and risked being crushed in its bite and devoured. But God had reached out for her and snatched her from between its jaws. She had felt Him at her side, guiding her every action. And that closeness was all the reward she needed.

MeAm Loez, Bemidbar, *BeHa'alotcha,*
pp. 98-104

פיה פתחה בחכמה.....
She opens her mouth
with wisdom....

*A ll her words are said with
wisdom.*

(Metzudat David, Mishlei 31:26)

No Need to Add a Word

"Father, go to bed," whispered Caesar's daughter. "It's past midnight."

The emperor raised his head from the pile of manuscripts scattered over his desk in the palace library. Stubs of candles on a tray before him flickered weakly in a pool of melted wax.

"One more minute..." he mumbled as he blinked back the sleep from his eyes and straightened himself in his chair. "You go on and get some rest. Don't worry about me."

Caesar's daughter closed the door quietly behind her. She knew that her father would still be at his desk when she rose the next morning.

This was not the first time he had spent the night poring over his books. It would certainly not be the last. Whenever the Jewish sages were planning to visit Rome, Caesar cloistered himself in his library, dismissing from his mind all the concerns of his nation. Like a man set on climbing a huge mountain, its peak hidden in the clouds, the emperor was obsessed with finding a question that the Hebrew scholars could not answer. He knew it was an impossible goal, but he could not resist trying.

His daughter would often listen in on these debates. She was fascinated by the ease with which the sages invariably replied. After many hours studying the ancient texts, her father always discovered a contradiction that shook the very foundation of Torah logic, but time and again the rabbis clarified it with little effort.

"I doubt he will ever succeed," thought Caesar's daughter as she blew out her lantern for the night.

❧

Caesar sat impatiently on his throne, sending a servant to check the outer hall every few minutes. The deep purple of his robe only underscored his pale, tired features.

Footsteps were heard on the marble entrance floor. Caesar leaned forward to catch a glimpse of his visitors.

"It's only me, Father," Caesar's daughter said as she took a seat at his side. "Haven't the Hebrew scholars arrived yet?"

"They're not supposed to be here for another hour or so," admitted Caesar. "But I'm so excited, I can't keep my mind on anything else."

"Oh, Father!" she laughed affectionately. "I bet you've come up with a real challenge this time!"

Caesar basked in her curiosity. "Just wait and see," he smiled.

At exactly the appointed hour, Rabban Gamliel and two disciples entered the throne room.

"Blessed are You, O Lord, our God, King of the Universe, Who has given of His glory to human beings!" the sage pronounced as he first caught sight of the emperor.

"Amen!" echoed the rabbis at his side.

Caesar beamed. What a wonderful religion this was to mandate the recitation of a special blessing upon seeing a powerful ruler!

His servants surrounded the rabbis with trays of fruit and pitchers of cold water. Summer days in Rome were as merciless as in the Land of Israel, and the men were parched from their walk to the palace.

"Your God is a thief!" the emperor charged as soon as they were seated. "Isn't it written that God put Adam to sleep and then took one of his ribs?"

Rabban Gamliel was about to reply when Caesar's daughter called out, "Summon the captain of the guards! Bring him here at once!"

All heads turned in her direction.

"What's the matter?" asked her father in alarm.

"I just remembered what happened last night," she said. "Thieves broke into the palace. They stole a silver pitcher and replaced it with a gold one!"

"That's what you're shouting about? Replacing silver with gold?" laughed Caesar with relief. "I wish thieves like that would come every day!"

His daughter looked at him with satisfaction.

"Listen to your own words," she said. "Do you think Adam complained about losing one small bone when he received a wife in exchange?"

The emperor looked in astonishment at his clever daughter. He was glad she had inherited some of his own sharpness.

"I will agree that the trade was in Adam's favor," he conceded to her. "But God still acted like a thief. Why did He put Adam to sleep? Why not carry out the exchange openly?"

Caesar's daughter thought back to her engagement banquet of the week before and the Roman matron who had sat beside her. Gazing at the woman's thick, gray hair and green eyes speckled with gold, Caesar's daughter had no trouble imagining how beautiful she must have been as a young girl.

"There is one thing you must always remember, my dear," the matron had said between delicate spoonfuls of broth. "No matter how attractive you are, you must always maintain a certain distance and dignity.

"I can tell you from my own experience," she added as she lowered her voice confidentially. "I had been betrothed to my uncle ever since I was a child. Our families all lived together on our grandparents' estate. He was a brilliant boy, only a few years older. It seemed like a perfect match. But," she raised a finger for emphasis, "because we grew up in the same home, I became unappealing in his eyes. In the end, he married another woman. And I can tell you," the matron winked, "she wasn't half as attractive as I."

Rabban Gamliel, his disciples, and all the ministers in the room waited in silence for Caesar's daughter to answer her father. But again she surprised them by issuing a strange command.

"Bring me a piece of raw meat!" she instructed a servant.

The servant returned with a slab of red beef lying on a silver tray in a pool of blood.

"Now bring me a knife, some coals, and a grill," she commanded.

The daughter drained off some of the blood, hacked away large chunks of fat, and cut up the meat. Then she roasted it in Caesar's presence.

"May I serve you?" she asked her father as she placed a sizzling portion of steak before him.

Caesar looked away, his facing taking on a greenish hue.

"I cannot eat," he mumbled. "It is so...unappealing."

"Isn't that just how Adam would have felt about his new bride had he been awake to witness her transformation?" said Caesar's daughter softly.

Rabban Gamliel nodded his head in silent approval. For once he had no need to add a word.

Bereishit Rabbah 17:7
Sanhedrin 39a and Rashi ad loc.

...וְתוֹרַת חֶסֶד עַל לְשׁוֹנָהּ.

*...and a lesson of kindness
is on her tongue.*

*S*he teaches the meaning of
true kindness.

(Metzudat David, Mishlei 31:26)

Serving the Servant of Israel

*R*ebbi's maidservant stiffened as she heard her master screaming once again. Gripping her broom tightly, she tried not to tremble as his cries grew stronger. To hear him in his pain was almost more than she could bear.

Everyone in the house dreaded these attacks, each one enduring them in his own way.

"Why do you wait so long between feedings?" the maidservant once asked the stablemaster who cared for Rebbi's hundreds of stallions. "By the time you bring their oats, they're so hungry they whinny at the top of their lungs. I bet they can be heard for miles!"

"Yes," the stablemaster nodded, "I'm sure they can be." Then he lowered his eyes in shame. "I don't mean to make the horses suffer, but their noise brings me some relief...."

Yes, she had noticed that he always waited for one of Rebbi's attacks before bringing out the fodder. Surely the stablemaster hoped to drown out his master's cries. But Rebbi's voice could be heard even above the tumult of the stable.

The maidservant shuddered. Rebbi had been wracked with severe illness for thirteen years now, and she knew that his was no ordinary suffering. She understood, as did her master, what had caused its sudden onset. The encounter that had seemed so innocent years earlier was drawn clearly in her mind:

A young calf was being led to the slaughterhouse when suddenly it broke away from its owner. It bolted to where Rebbi sat learning in his garden and hid its head in the folds of his robe. The calf bleated in terror, and to the maidservant it seemed to be pleading for mercy.

But Rebbi shooed the animal out of his lap. "Go on," he said. "That's what you were created for."

As far as the maidservant could remember, this was the moment her master's health had left him. Surely it had been said in Heaven: "Since he has no pity on the calf, let suffering come upon him."

As Rebbi's groans subsided, the maidservant eased her grip upon the broom and threw herself into her chores with renewed vigor. It felt good to attack the dusty corners of the room. If only she could so easily do away with her master's illness.

She slammed the broom in frustration, and something scurried past. Bending down, she spied a litter of mice huddled under a dresser. They were curled up onto one another, oblivious to the tension in their home.

The maidservant poked at them with her broom. "Out! Out!" she hissed impatiently. "Be gone with you! Make your home somewhere else."

At that moment, Rebbi stepped slowly into the room. His faced showed the strain of his latest bout with pain.

"Let them be," he whispered hoarsely, motioning towards the mice. "Let them be. God has mercy on all His creatures."

The maidservant loosened her hold on the broom and looked up at her master's face. Color she had not seen for years was returning to his cheeks. Muscles that had grown knotted were beginning to relax. Her eyes met his, and at once she knew.

The decree had just been lifted. Her master was cured.

Rabbi Yehudah HaNasi, known as Rebbi, was the last of the great rabbis called the Tannaim. He was born on the day of Rabbi Akiva's death, and the sages later observed: "A sun has risen and a sun has set."

Rebbi served his people faithfully and was fortunate to have a maidservant who served him with equal devotion. Her concern for her master extended to his many disciples as well.

She never liked to give the students orders. Instead she spoke to them in riddles.

"The ladle strikes against the jar; let the eagles fly to their nests," she would tell the young men when the beverages were finished and they could leave the dining room.

And when she wished them to remain at the table, she would say, "The ladle floats in the jar like a ship that sails the sea."

Once, the maidservant passed a student and his father in the public square. The man was enraged at his grown son, beating him and berating him loudly. The maidservant took the father aside and spoke to him softly.

"Be careful not to put a stumbling block before your son," she pleaded. "If you shame him in public, he may become even more rebellious. He may even strike you in return—a very serious crime!"

At times, she was totally unaware of the help she supplied the scholars; it seemed to be orchestrated from Above.

Rebbi's students were once stymied in their learning because they did not know the meaning of the Aramaic words *serugin* (intervals), *chaluglogot* (vegetable greens), and *metateh* (broom). They also disagreed on who should take precedence, the wisest or the oldest.

"Let's go to Rebbi's house and ask," they resolved.

The large group arrived at their teacher's door but could not decide who among them should enter first.

As they stood outside debating the matter, the maidservant came to the door.

"Go in according to age," she instructed.

The students began to enter slowly, a few at a time.

"Why are you going in by *serugin*?" she asked them.

Finally all the disciples had come inside except for one, who was carrying a bulky sack of parsley sprigs. As he tried to fit through the doorway, the sack slipped off his shoulder and burst open on the ground.

"Young man," the maidservant chided him, "your *chaluglogot* have fallen all over the floor. I will get the *metateh* and sweep them up!"

❦

Even in Rebbi's very last moments, his faithful maidservant continued to serve him.

Passing by the old sage's room, the maidservant heard him groaning in pain. She remembered his suffering of years before but knew that this time the decree would not be lifted.

At the age of one hundred twenty, Rabbi Yehudah lay close to death, but his disciples refused to let him go. They could not imagine life without their master.

"We'll call a public fast," one student suggested. "None of us will eat or sleep. We'll stand and pray outside Rebbi's home until he's cured."

"Let's not forget the power of our words," an older scholar added. "We must be careful not to open our mouths to evil."

"That's right!" his friend broke in. "Whoever says that Rebbi is dying should be pierced with a sword!"

While the disciples stood in agitated groups outside their master's door, Rebbi's maidservant climbed up to the rooftop. Raising her hands Heavenward, she cried out, "Master of the Universe! The angels are demanding that Rebbi join them, and the students are demanding that he remain on earth. May the ones below overpower the ones above!"

The Heavenly soldiers remained at their posts, the earthly soldiers at theirs, and Rebbi's life hung in the balance, equally claimed by two worlds.

As the day of prayers wore on, the maidservant stood by Rebbi's side. Only she could truly judge the ravages of age and illness. His skin had grown pale and thin over the years; it now looked almost transparent. And the scholar's frail body rested weightlessly on the bed as if not really touching it.

The maidservant looked into his eyes, afraid to see the agony they surely held, but she saw only blissful calm.

"Separating the soul from the body is as difficult as disentangling a ball of yarn from a thornbush," she had been taught. Why did her master seem so peaceful despite his suffering?

She knew that the body must return to dust and the soul to the One who gave it. But since most souls develop a strong attachment to the body, they have a hard time extricating themselves at the time of death. Only those few righteous people whose souls are never shackled by the body find eternal rest without hindrance.

Rabbi Yehudah HaNasi was one of them.

But something was holding him back. His soul was trying to depart, yet it was blocked by some force beyond his control.

"I must serve him now," thought the maidservant without hesitation, "as I have all these years."

For the second time that day, she climbed to the rooftop and turned her eyes towards Heaven. "Creator of man," she began, "may Your mercy allow the ones above to prevail over the ones below!"

As she begged for the blessed relief of death, the disciples outside Rebbi's room continued to pray that he be spared.

It was a stalemate.

Rebbi's maidservant searched for a way to carry out her last act of service. Suddenly, her eyes fell upon a pile of discarded earthenware in a corner of the rooftop. She lifted one vessel and turned it over in her hands.

The clay pot was cracked and chipped in many places. It seemed that it would crumble under the slightest pressure. Yes, nodded the maidservant, every pot must one day crack and crumble from daily use. And every man worn with age must one day die. He may live to seventy or one hundred, or even one hundred twenty, but the time will come when his body becomes a shattered and useless vessel. Surely that is the time to praise God for death, just as one praises Him for life.

From the rooftop, she raised the pot above her head and hurled it to the ground. As it shattered in all directions, the scholars were jolted from their prayers for a brief moment.

During this pause, Rabbi Yehudah was free to die.

"Our master is gone!" the disciples cried. "The angels have overpowered us mortals, and the 'holy ark' has been taken!"

Rabbi Yehudah HaNasi served Israel in holiness and purity. Surely the "Servant of Israel" could have had no better servant than the maidservant of Rebbi.

Kohelet Rabbah 7:11
Bava Metzia 84b, 85a
Megillah 18a
Rosh HaShanah 26b
Ketubot 104a
Jerusalem Talmud, *Megillah* 2:2; *Kilaim* 9:4

צופיה הליכות ביתה....

She oversees the ways
of her household....

*A*nd she said to her husband, "Behold, now I perceive that this is a holy man of God who passes by us continually."

(II Melachim 4:9)

The Words of a Prophet

I know this man is different," the Shunamite woman whispered to her husband. "He shouldn't have to sit together with the others."

Her husband followed her glance over to where their guests were relaxing after dinner. The stranger she had spoken about nodded pleasantly as the conversation flowed around him, but he was clearly deep in his own thoughts.

"Call it woman's intuition," she insisted. "Call it experience."

Her husband smiled. Experience was one thing his wife had in abundance. Did anyone in Shunam take care of as many guests as she?

Of course, travelers were welcome in plenty of homes, but only she actually sought them out. She checked the synagogues and study halls at the end of the day to see if anyone remained behind. She questioned the wagon drivers regularly to find out if they had brought new arrivals into town. And when she finally tracked down a stranger, she would not relent until he had agreed to stay at her home for the remainder of his visit.

"Yes," her husband thought, "I have not seen a traveler yet who can pass through our town undetected."

But now she was insisting that this stranger needed a room of his own; that he shouldn't have to eat and sleep in the company of the other visitors.

"He does seem to be a thoughtful sort," her husband conceded. "Perhaps an artist or a teacher. But why a special room?"

"He must have privacy...to meditate.... A woman knows the nature of her guests. This one is a holy man."

Her husband stared at her in astonishment. "Holy?"

"Yes, a great Torah scholar, a righteous man; perhaps even a prophet...." A shiver ran through her body. "Look closely," she instructed. "Even the flies sense that he is a man of God. They never go near his plate, yet they keep coming back to the others'.

"I just know he shouldn't have to sit there," she declared. "He has already passed through our town several times in recent months. I'm sure he will continue to stop by. We should set up a small room, maybe near the attic, with a bed, a table, a chair, a lamp—"

"Wait," her husband stopped her. "What about the boy who always comes with him? Don't we need to make a special place for him, too?"

The Shunamite woman raised her head and studied the scene in the next room. Her guests were still seated around the table, their empty plates pushed towards the center as they leaned back in their chairs. The stranger sat apart but his young companion—his assistant, she decided—leaned forward with great interest. His eyes turned sharply from one speaker to the next so as not to miss a word. When she saw that he was greedily clutching a large chunk of bread, despite the many loaves still on the table, she answered decisively, "No. The boy can remain with the others."

The Shunamite woman straightened the chair and ran a finger over the tabletop to check for dust. Then she adjusted the lamp and smoothed the bedcovers. With her back to the window, she surveyed the small room. Yes, everything was in place. And it was so quiet up here, away from her busy household. The stranger had returned this afternoon. She was sure he would be pleased.

She turned and looked out the window just in time to see her husband coming up the path on his way home from the evening prayers.

"Come on down! I have something to tell you!" he called up to her.

He took her over to a quiet corner and whispered, "You were right! You were right after all! Do you know who that stranger is?"

The Shunamite woman shook her head in bewilderment.

"He's none other than Elisha the prophet!"

"Elisha the prophet?" the Shunamite woman gasped. "The disciple of Elijah?"

"That's right," nodded her husband. "Today he spoke in the synagogue, and people were whispering about his identity. But you..." he stopped and looked at his wife with admiration. "You sensed it all along."

❦

The Shunamite woman bent over the large bowl and examined the foaming yeast. She sniffed the mixture and poked it with her finger. Almost ready, she thought. It just needs to sit near the oven for a few more minutes. But as she moved the bowl, she felt a presence behind her. Someone was in the room. Glancing up, she was startled to find the prophet's assistant gazing at her from the kitchen doorway. She lowered her batter with shaking hands, glad she had not spilled it in surprise. Would she ever get used to this brash young man?

"Yes, Gechazi," she sighed. "What is it?"

"My master wishes to speak to you," he said with a grin.

She washed her hands quickly and dusted off her apron. Was everything all right? she wondered as she made her way up the stairs.

The Shunamite woman stood outside the door as Gechazi announced her arrival. What could the prophet want so urgently?

She was totally unprepared for what followed.

"You have gone to so much trouble for us," Elisha told her. "How can I repay you? Perhaps you have a special need that I can pray for?"

His hostess was astounded. Repay her? Special prayers? Who could refuse the intervention of a holy man? Yet special prayers were the last thing she wanted. Surely the prophet knew that by asking for favors, she would be exposing herself to God's scrutiny. Once she singled herself out for attention, all her deeds would be judged. Did she dare put herself in such danger?

"No, my master," she bowed respectfully. "I prefer to add my prayers to those of my people. I will fare much better as part of the nation."

But Elisha was determined. After she had descended the stairs, he turned to his assistant.

"There must be *something* we can do for her!"

"There is," smiled Gechazi as he revealed what he had learned from the other guests. "They are quite old, but they have never had children."

Elisha nodded. "Call her back," he commanded the boy.

"I insist on giving you a blessing," said the prophet when she returned. "Next year at this time, you shall hold a son in your arms!"

The Shunamite woman trembled. Was there any greater gift? Would all her years of waiting soon be over? She leaned against the wall and closed her eyes as if to trap the vision before it vanished.

"Next year at this time..."—where had she heard this before? "Hold a son in your arms..."—why did these words bother her? She tried to banish the unpleasant thoughts that pushed into her mind. Here was a prophet of the Lord giving her his blessing, yet she couldn't help picking at the words. Something was not right....

"Excuse me, my master," she turned to Elisha. "You say, 'Next year at this time...' just as the angels told our mother Sarah. But they also promised that they themselves would be back at that time to guarantee the fulfillment of their words, whereas you have not said that you will return...."

Elisha shook his head emphatically. "There is no reason to worry," he calmed her. "Angels, who live forever, can easily promise to return. Can I, a mortal, make such a commitment? One day I am alive and the next day, who knows? But whether I am alive or dead, you shall have your son."

The Shunamite woman nodded as she thought over his words. But she still had one more reservation.

"You promise that I shall hold a son *in my arms*. Shall I only have him as a child to hold in my arms, or will he remain with me longer? I beg you, O man of God, do not deceive me with a blessing short-lived...."

The Shunamite woman gazed up at her husband as he lifted the sleeping bundle by her side. Swaddled in soft cotton, the newborn was spent from his long birth. His mother lay weakly on her bed. What a struggle it had been for them to separate from one another. Could a man ever understand? She felt as if she had been pulled to the edge of death and back again; as if her every limb had to be wrenched out of place and refashioned in order to transform her into a mother. And here stood her husband, the same as always, yet now a father.

"Do you know what day it is?" he asked his wife as he cradled his new son in his arms. "It is exactly one year from the day the prophet blessed you!"

"When a righteous person makes a decree," she said, "the Almighty carries it out."

It's impossible to keep a child home forever, the Shunamite women reminded herself as she drew the curtains in the front room. Her son had begged to watch his father reaping, but perhaps she shouldn't have let him go out to the field on such a hot day. It was not yet noon and the sun was already blinding. The house felt as if it would catch fire any minute and explode into embers. What must it be like outdoors? Would her husband make sure their son found shade?

Suddenly one of the field hands burst through the door, holding the young boy against his chest.

"What's the matter?" gasped his mother as she ran to take him.

"He was sitting and watching us work," explained the man, "when suddenly he clutched his head and began to rock back and forth in pain. He kept screaming: 'My head! My head!' His father told me to bring him home. It must have been the sun...."

The Shunamite woman was barely listening. She was too busy putting wet cloths on his head to fight the heat within him.

"You can go back now," she told the worker as she poured her son some water and urged him to drink.

The boy curled up in her lap and fell into a deep sleep. His head dropped back and his breathing became labored. Hours passed as she clutched him to her, rocking him with the rhythm of her prayers. And all the while the words of the prophet ran through her mind: "You shall hold a son *in your arms....*"

All at once his body seemed to weigh more heavily upon her. His breathing had ceased and his eyes rolled back. "*In your arms.... In your arms....*" Yes, she now held a son in her arms. Dead in her arms....

The Shunamite woman lifted the boy's limp body and climbed the stairs to Elisha's room. She laid him gently on the prophet's bed.

It's over now, she told herself. What could be more final than death? Even King David knew when to accept God's judgment. He fasted for days when his son took ill, but after the child died he rose from the floor and asked for bread. There was nothing more to be done. You hope, you pray, you fight until the last moment. And now the last moment had come.

Yet a voice within her cried, "No! This is different. The prophet gave you his word...."

She walked out to the front yard. There was her husband, just back from the field.

"Please send me a servant and a donkey," she called to him. "I must go to Mount Carmel to see the prophet."

"Why today?" asked her husband in surprise. "It's not the new moon, nor is the Sabbath approaching...."

The Shunamite woman bit her lip and looked away. No, it was not the first day of the month, when she would ride her donkey to the most distant towns to hear words of Torah. Nor was it the holy day of rest, when she would walk to any scholar or holy man in the vicinity. Today there was a different reason for her to run to the prophet, but she would not share it—even with her husband. She would not open her mouth to evil. The words of the holy man still held their power and she would say nothing to work against them.

Instead, she simply saddled her donkey, whispered "Shalom," and departed.

The prophet had to bring back her son, she resolved as she made her way up the hill. She would not return until he agreed to come with her.

Elisha lifted his eyes and saw her making her way up the mountain.

"Here comes that Shunamite woman!" he called to Gechazi. "Something must be the matter. Run to her and ask her what has happened!"

But the bereaved mother refused to tell Gechazi, either. "All is well," she answered calmly.

When she reached the prophet, however, she fell at his feet and grasped his legs. Gechazi sought to push her away, but Elisha held him back.

"Leave her!" he commanded. "Her soul is bitter and the Almighty has hidden the reason from me."

The Shunamite woman raised her head and cried out, "Did I ask my master for a son? Didn't I say, 'Do not deceive me?' Better a vessel should remain forever empty than be filled only to be spilled to the ground!"

Elisha opened his eyes in alarm.

"Something has happened to the child!" he shouted to Gechazi. "Run to the boy and place my staff on his face that he may live."

Then the prophet paused and looked at Gechazi solemnly. "I am sending you as my messenger," he added. "You must be careful. Do not disgrace the miracle by calling attention to it. Don't even greet the people you pass on your way. And if they greet you, do not respond."

As Gechazi clutched the staff and dashed off, Elisha imagined that the miracle would soon occur.

But the Shunamite woman knew better. She had long ago perceived the true nature of this servant, and she had little confidence in him. She would surely not leave her son's fate in his hands.

"It is not enough!" she persisted. "I shall not leave until you come with me!"

"But I have sent my servant and instructed him not to speak. He will be acting as an extension of myself, like my arm or my staff."

"Yes," said the Shunamite, "if he decides to follow your instructions...."

The prophet frowned and rose to follow her.

Gechazi ran through the hills waving the prophet's staff above his head. He had been sent on many strange missions but this was the most bizarre of all.

What was this staff but a simple piece of wood? Did Elisha think it had magical powers?

"I'm going to revive the dead!" he boasted to everyone he passed. "This staff can do miracles!" Then he broke into peals of laughter.

Gechazi climbed the stairs to his master's room and flung open the door. There was the boy. Now all he had to do was put the staff on his face....

But nothing happened. Gechazi waited expectantly but there was no sound, no movement. What had he done wrong? Hadn't he done what his master told him?

Gechazi began to tremble. What would the prophet do to him when he found out he had not saved the boy? He hurried out of the house and back towards Mount Carmel. This time he did not say a word to anyone.

He met Elisha and the Shunamite woman on the way.

"The boy has not stirred," he told them nervously.

Elisha quickened his steps and headed towards the house. He had no time to wonder what Gechazi had done to prevent the miracle. Now he had to pray that much harder. He quickly climbed to his chamber and closed the door behind him.

Elisha prayed, but he couldn't have prayed as fervently as the Shunamite woman waiting below. She understood that Elisha was merely God's messenger. Only God Himself could give her back her son.

The prophet placed his mouth on the boy's mouth, his eyes on the boy's eyes, his palms on the boy's palms. He knew that these acts alone had no effect on the dead, but he had to employ natural means as much as was possible. Only when he had done all he could would the Almighty take over and work wonders.

Slowly, the boy's flesh began to warm. Elisha rose and paced the room; then he touched the boy again.

Suddenly, the boy sneezed seven times and opened his eyes.

"Call the mother," Elisha commanded Gechazi, who had waited in trepidation outside the door. "Her son is alive. Tell her to come and see."

The Shunamite woman made her way up the narrow stairs, but she really did not need to see at all. The words of the prophet were enough for her. They always had been.

Bereishit 18:10 and Rashi ad loc.
II Melachim 4:8-37 and Ralbag,
   Rashi, Metzudat David, Radak,
   and Malbim ad loc.
Berachot 10b
Mussar HaNeviim
Rabbi Simchah Zissel Ziv, *Chochmah
   U'Mussar*, vol. I, p. 96

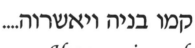

קמו בניה ויאשרוה....

*Her sons rise and
laud her....*

*T*hey said [to Rabbi Chanina ben Tradion],
"What do you see?"
"I see only the parchment consumed; the
letters fly up into the air!"

Bruriah, the wife of Rabbi Meir, was the
daughter of Rabbi Chanina ben Tradion.

(Avodah Zarah 18a)

❧

Only the Parchment

*B*ruriah stood at the back of the study hall, surveying the tumult of Torah learning. Fists pounding on tables, hands waving in the air, heads nodding in excitement. But what pleased her most was the din of excited voices arguing, explaining, discovering.... Here and there a student sang out the passage he was working on; at times it was a song of sudden revelation, and at times a meditative chant of concentration.

She closed her eyes as the sounds weaved around her. "There is no music more pleasing than that of Torah," she thought.

Indeed, as a child the song of Torah study had been her lullaby. The voices of her father learning with his disciples had soothed her to sleep at night and greeted her ears when she woke in the morning.

They never seemed to cease.

Bruriah looked around the room once more. Suddenly her gaze rested upon one young student sitting perfectly still over his books. He made no movement and no sound escaped his lips. It was profoundly disturbing, as if a member of the choir had suddenly refused to sing his part, standing impassively as the harmony rose up around him.

She waited until the young man sat at her table later that day.

"You must know," she said to him gently, "that if your learning permeates your entire being, then it will be successful. As King David said, 'All my limbs shall proclaim: Lord, who is like You...?' But if you do not use your faculty of speech, your learning will not remain with you. See if you can immerse yourself entirely in Torah and not hold back."

Of the countless Jewish women who have immersed themselves in Torah, Bruriah is the most famous. Torah was her first love and its words guided every facet of her life.

Bruriah knew that the physical body has no life of its own. Only the God-given soul within animates its limbs. But she also knew that sometimes the flesh abducts the pure soul and compels it to act against its will.

She remembered the afternoon her husband, Rabbi Meir, came home unusually troubled. "It's those lowlifes again," he sighed as he met her questioning gaze. "They are terrorizing everyone in the community. It seems that they will give their fellow Jews no peace as long as they live."

He paused and lowered his voice in anguish. "May God take them from this world...."

Bruriah inhaled sharply.

"I know you've tried everything with these people," she said, "yet they continue to plague our city. But how do you know you're allowed to pray for their death? Where have you learned such a thing?"

This was just the sort of question expected from Bruriah. Most people would have asked if his prayer was kind and proper and moral. But for Bruriah this was insufficient. She demanded to know his source in either the written or the oral Torah. What verse had he based his decisions on, and had he interpreted that verse correctly?

Of course, he had considered this question before uttering his prayer. "Doesn't it say in Tehillim, 'Let sinners cease from the earth and let the wicked be no more...'?" he countered.

Bruriah shook her head slowly. "I always understood it to mean, 'Let *sins* cease from the earth....' Why pray for sinners to die? If you pray that they change their ways, they will no longer be wicked!"

"How can I pray for them to change their ways?" asked Rabbi Meir in surprise. "The sages have already taught, 'All is in the hands of Heaven except for the fear of Heaven.' If these people do not choose to be God-fearing by their own free will, no prayer to God can force them."

"That's only true of people who intentionally choose to be wicked. But most souls yearn to be good. They are simply swayed by external pressures like bad company, extreme poverty, or even too much wealth. We must not judge them, for they are virtually forced to sin."

"So you are suggesting that I pray for the Almighty to remove the obstacles to their repentance?"

"Yes," said Bruriah. "It's certainly worth a try."

Rabbi Meir heeded her words, and God heard his prayers: the persecution of the community ceased.

❦

Bruriah stretched her arms and raised her head from the Torah portion she was studying. As usual on Sabbath afternoons, Rabbi Meir was at the study hall giving his regular lesson, and their two sons were up in their room challenging each other with a knotty Talmudic problem.

Bruriah smiled as she listened to her children. She was glad to see her sons' love of Torah and passion for truth, which had been kindled early on by their parents.

She thought back to the previous evening and her husband and children singing "A Woman of Valor" as they did every Friday night. The same verses always made her stop and think:

Her husband's heart trusts in her....

She opens her mouth with wisdom, and a lesson of kindness is on her tongue.

Her sons arise and laud her, and her husband praises her.

She often asked herself how well she embodied these words. Surely she had occasionally opened her mouth with wisdom, but had she done so with kindness and compassion? And could her husband truly put his trust in her? Did she think solely of his welfare in his time of need? Was she truly "a woman of valor," worthy of her family's praise?

Bruriah shivered and returned to her reading. Yet something was wrong. The letters blurred before her eyes and refused to make sense. Lifting her head from the book, she noticed that her sons had suddenly become still. That stillness was more disturbing than any noise could have been.

She jumped up and ran to the stairs. The silence pressed in upon her and she could barely breathe. Pulling herself up by the railing, she burst into the upper room.

There, she saw her sons still at the table, still clutching their books, their heads dropped lifelessly before them....

As she stood in shock, the years seemed to fall away. She was once again a young girl, watching the flames leap before her eyes....

Standing near the pit, she could see the kindling quickly catching fire, and there, in the center of the blaze....

"Father! Father!" she cried. "What are they doing to you?"

She screamed in horror, but her voice was swallowed up by the roar of the Roman crowds surging forward to view the execution. The firewood crackled and tongues of flame licked at her father's flesh. Bruriah could feel the heat singeing her hair.

She gazed at her father's tortured face. Just a few

hours earlier, he had been teaching his disciples from the precious Torah scroll he always kept at his side. It was one of the few that the Romans had not yet confiscated. But suddenly the soldiers had rushed in and seized him, calling the public to witness another execution.

In death as in life, Rabbi Chanina ben Tradion was not parted from his beloved Torah, for they had wrapped the scroll around his body. The parchment rapidly caught flame, but his own end was not as quick. To prolong his agony, the executioner had placed wet cloths over his heart.

Bruriah gasped for air.

"Father!" she cried. "How can I see you like this? Is this the reward for a life of Torah?"

Out of the flames, Rabbi Chanina managed to reply: "If I were being burned alone, it would be difficult for me to bear. But now that I am being burned together with the Torah, I am confident that the One Who avenges the disgrace of the Torah will avenge my disgrace as well."

Suddenly a great, thunderous roar was heard overhead. Rabbi Chanina's eyes grew wide, yet even as his disciples craned their necks skyward, they saw nothing.

"Rebbe! What do you see?" they asked.

"I see only the parchment consumed; the letters fly up into the air! The flesh is scorched, but the spirit returns home...."

❦

Slowly the flames began to recede, and there before her were her sons, slumped over their books.

The same words resounded in her mind: "Is this the reward for a life of Torah?" But the same comfort mingled with her grief. In death as in life, they were not parted from the holy Torah. They had been learning up to the very last moment, and had died amid their books. Their souls had accomplished their mission in this world and had now returned home with all the holiness they had gleaned here.

"How foolish we are to rejoice over birth and weep over death," she remembered learning. "When a child is born, we should weep over the perilous voyage ahead of him. What dangers lurk out there? Will he ever reach safe shores? But when a person dies after a life of righteousness, it is cause for joy. He has ventured down to the depths and escaped with precious spoils." Bruriah knew that she could only grieve for herself, not for her sons, for they had succesfully completed their journey.

She gathered up her eldest son and cradled his body in her arms. Gently, she laid him on the bed. Then she lifted up her younger son and placed him beside his brother. She gave each one a parting kiss and spread a sheet over them, securely tucking in the covers as she had so often done on cold, windy nights.

Passing by their table, she closed their books. "The letters fly up," she reminded herself. "Only the parchment is consumed...."

Stars were already making their way across the horizon. The Sabbath had ended, and Bruriah knew her husband would be home shortly. Her eyes burned with the sting of unshed tears, but this was not the time to let them flow.

Rabbi Meir took his coat off slowly as he entered the room. He always moved with effort after teaching, for the Torah seemed to sap his strength.

"Where are the boys?" he asked, looking around.

"They've gone to study," replied Bruriah.

"But I just came from the study hall and did not see them."

Bruriah responded by handed him a cup of *Havdalah* wine. Yet the service did not distract Rabbi Meir from his unanswered question.

"Where are the boys?" he repeated.

Bruriah seemed unconcerned. "They went somewhere. They may be back any moment," she said as she poured him a bowl of hot soup.

As she went about her housework, her husband began to relax. The steaming broth warmed him, and he felt his strength begin to return.

When he had finished, Bruriah sat beside him.

"Before the Sabbath, a man left some valuables in my trust," she said. "He asked me to guard them until he returned. He has now come back and asked for his belongings. Must I return them?"

Rabbi Meir stared at her in astonishment. This was not the kind of question he expected to hear from his scholarly wife.

"My dear one," he replied at once, "when one guards a deposit, is he not obliged to return it to its rightful owner?"

Bruriah nodded silently and led her husband upstairs. She brought him near the bed and lifted the sheet.

There lay their two sons, without a breath of life.

"My sons! My sons!" Rabbi Meir cried out. Falling

into a chair, he sobbed until it seemed his frail body would burst. "My teachers! My teachers!" he wept. "You were my sons in the eyes of the world, but in my eyes you were also my teachers, enlightening me with your Torah!"

"Rebbe," Bruriah whispered, "did you not say that we are obliged to return valuables whenever the rightful owner claims them? Our children were never our own possessions. They were only left with us for safekeeping. God gave them, and now God has taken them back."

Rabbi Meir's sobs began to subside. He looked over at his wife and understood that they had been chosen as the guardians of two precious souls during their short stay on earth. And he knew that they had been proper caretakers, for not only had their sons departed without blemish, they had even attained their unique portions of truth. Surely their souls had returned with the fire of Torah burning brightly within them.

Bruriah had comforted her husband. She had not indulged in her own sorrow until she had prepared him for his loss. In her great wisdom, she had helped him let go of the precious sons who were no longer in his possession.

Rabbi Meir knew that he could always trust in Bruriah. In his grief, he praised her. And he was certain that in the world of truth, their sons were rising up to laud her as well.

Midrash Shochar Tov, Mishlei 31
Kohelet Rabbah 7a
Eiruvin 53b
Berachot 10a and *Anaf Yosef* ad loc.
Avodah Zarah 18a and Tosafot, Maharal,
    and *Ben Ish Chai* ad loc.
Beit HaLevi on the Torah, second part, p. 16

...וִיהַלְלוּהָ בַשְּׁעָרִים מַעֲשֶׂיהָ.

*...and let her deeds praise
her in the gates.*

*W*e will be glad and rejoice
[only] in You.

(Shir HaShirim 1:4)

No Greater Treasure

*T*he woman of Sidon moved her finger aimlessly along the windowpane. The stone path leading out to her garden and the fruit trees beyond seemed to swim before her eyes. Was it the raindrops that poured down from the leaden sky, or the tears that threatened to gush forth any moment?

She watched her servants hurrying to unhitch the last of the donkeys from their wagons before the rains grew stronger. The beasts brayed impatiently as the sudden wind whipped about their legs. Soon the caravan was dismantled and the workmen ran for cover.

She and her husband had returned that day from a journey to Israel's greatest sage, Rabbi Shimon bar Yochai, traveling for days to hear him confirm what they had already decided. But who could have expected his strange stipulation?

"Make a festive meal, a 'mitzvah meal,'" the rabbi's words echoed in her mind. "Celebrate. Rejoice. Just the two of you. Set out your best dishes."

The sage had looked from one dejected face to the other.

"Do as I tell you," he urged them. "It will all be for the best."

❦

For years the Creator had withheld His blessing and the woman of Sidon had remained childless. As the years slipped away, her hopes went with them.

"What are we doing?" she questioned her husband. "Just spending our years together? In the end we will leave this world the same as we found it. Isn't it better to separate now so you can try to start a family for yourself?"

Her husband shook his head wearily. "I know you only want what is best for me," he sighed, "but I could never think of another woman. Why don't we just wait and see?"

"Wait for what?" she demanded. "A cold grave? No, it seems that we have no future. If God has not blessed us by now...."

That afternoon, they began their journey to Rabbi Shimon.

The venerable scholar heard their words and tried to console them. "Normally, when a husband and wife divorce it is such a tragedy that even the stones of the Temple altar weep," he said. "But you have not come in strife. You only wish to do the right thing.

"Years ago you came together to build a Jewish

family. Now you have decided to separate so that a family may yet be built. Years ago you celebrated your union with a festive meal and much joy. Now you must mark your separation the same way with food and drink and happiness. After all, you are still trying to do God's will...."

The rain grew stronger, pounding on the stones outside their home.

The woman of Sidon pictured the heavy baskets of produce her husband would be carrying from the market. "I hope he finds shelter until the storm subsides," she thought. Taking a handkerchief from an ivory box by her side, she wiped away her tears. Would she ever stop worrying over him? Would she ever be able to keep her thoughts from him once he was no longer hers?

She opened an old cedar chest and lifted out a silver tray, an heirloom her mother had given her on her wedding day.

She saw her mother before her once again:

"This tray has been in the family for years and years," she had told her. "I don't even know whom it first belonged to. It's been used at circumcisions for generations. I, too, carried in your newborn brothers on this tray."

The young bride had lifted the tray gently in her hands. In its polished surface, she saw her face shining with dreams of the future; of a time when she herself would be a mother...a grandmother...even a great-grandmother....

Now she unwrapped the yellowed paper that had covered the tray for so many years. The silver had not dulled; in fact, it was even more brilliant than she remembered. But in its reflection she no longer saw dreams, only her own features staring back at her.

"There's no reason to store it away anymore," she thought as she shut the old chest.

The woman of Sidon spread out her best linen and placed the tray in the center of the table. As she filled it with the fruits of her garden—large clusters of purple grapes, golden oranges, and plump, juicy dates—the intricate design in the silver was soon hidden from sight.

Her husband came in the door, leaving a puddle of water at his feet. He could hardly meet her eyes. "I found everything you asked for," he said quickly, trying to sound as if it were any ordinary shopping day. "There was almost no one out in the marketplace."

"It looks as if you got wet enough to make up for all the people who stayed home," she said with a small smile.

Later that evening, they sat at the table with little appetite, hardly tasting the tender veal she had prepared. Their attempts at conversation became strained as they thought of the reason for their feast. How often had they shared the day's events over a dinner not so different from tonight's, yet now their silence said more than words.

Her husband poured one glass of wine after another. Finally, she saw him relax from the burden of his heart.

"Look throughout the house," he said softly, "and

take whatever treasures you wish to your father's house."

She scanned the rooms that together they had called home. She was surrounded by things of beauty: she leaned back on thick, embroidered cushions; silk tapestries colored the walls; cabinets inlaid with precious stones held dishes of crystal. Yet there was no joy in any of it.

Her husband had fallen into a wine-clouded sleep on the couch, and she was glad he could escape the tension of the past few days. How contented he seemed at that moment. But who would care for him when she was gone?

Her body stiffened as she tried not to picture another woman at his side. Would a stranger understand him? Would she sense when he wished to be alone or when he longed for company? And what about children? They had spoken so much of their plans for them.... Would a new wife consider his feelings as she raised their family? Would she respect the things that he held dear?

The woman of Sidon surveyed the beautiful furnishings one last time and rose silently. She had made her choice. No doubts remained in her mind.

With a finger to her lips, she motioned to the servants in the adjoining room. "Shh. Don't wake him," she commanded in a whisper. "Pick up the couch and follow me."

Without a sound she slipped out the front door, and the unusual procession was on its way. She paid no attention to the curious stares of late-night strollers as she passed through the city streets. Her husband slept on, oblivious to the scene unfolding around him.

It was already past midnight when he finally opened his eyes.

"Where am I?" he said, looking over at his wife.

"You are in my father's house," she answered quietly.

"What am I doing here?"

She smiled at his confusion. "I did just what you told me to do," she explained. "You said, 'Take whatever treasures you wish to your father's house.'"

Her voice barely a whisper, she added, "I have no greater treasure in the world than you...."

In the morning they packed their wagons and again set out to see Rabbi Shimon bar Yochai.

Hearing their story, the sage saw something he had not seen before. They had decided to part, but it had not been so easy to accomplish.

"Return to your home in peace," he told them. "Your love continues to bind you together as if by some power of its own."

A cool breeze blew through the open window. It was one of the last days of autumn, just before homes are boarded up against the winter cold and each family is left alone to itself. This winter would be so different, mused the woman of Sidon as she unwrapped the silver tray for the second time in her life.

"Thank you, Mother," she thought.

People began to fill her living room, but she was not there to welcome them. In another part of the house, she was busy dressing her newborn son.

The home that had once been so empty could barely contain the many well-wishers being ushered in with laughter. Some tables were piled with tender meats; others with cakes and sweet fruits. Everyone crowded around the new father to bless him and his family.

Finally, it was time to bring the infant.

As the tiny baby was carried through the room, he seemed unimpressed by the many celebrants. Yet the same could not be said of them. Hundreds of eyes greeted him with fascination. Everyone knew that the little boy lying on the silver tray was a miracle.

The woman of Sidon comforted her son and put him to sleep; then she headed back to the celebration. Why was it so quiet? As she neared the doorway, she saw that her husband had already begun to speak. All heads were turned in his direction.

"If it were not for my wife's devotion," she heard him say, "our family would not exist today. The strength of her love built a home where there would have been nothing but ruin. And just as she has given us a new beginning, may our story give new hope to all who hear it."

In fact, their story gave new hope to the entire nation.

After standing as a bride at Mount Sinai and building a house for God in the Holy Land, the Jewish people saw that house destroyed. Yet because of their steadfast love of God, the bond between the Almighty and His people would not be severed.

Throughout the generations, their prayer has found expression in one woman's words: "We have no greater treasure in the world than You!"

Yalkut Shimoni, Bereishit 16, and *Zayit*
   Raanan ad loc.
Midrash Rabbah on Shir HaShirim 1:4

Epilogue

Within Jewish history, we find many outstanding women worthy of study and emulation. Their lands, dress and language may have varied, yet they all shared a singleminded dedication to perpetuating their heritage, building Jewish homes, and sanctifying God's name in the world.

Like a dominant gene that keeps recurring, these strengths have surfaced again and again throughout the generations. How many women have followed the example of Kimchit and kept their beauty hidden from the public eye—whether beneath the veil of Arab lands or under the woolen scarf of Eastern Europe? How many women learned from Bruriah's wisdom to comfort families scorched by the fires of persecution? How many found the strength to fight for the lives of their loved ones as did the wife of On ben Pelet, the Shunamite woman, and the thrice-widowed bride? Chanah's soul-searching prayers, the hospitality of Mar Ukva's wife, the attempts of Rabbi Chanina ben Dosa's wife to guard her family's dignity...all these acts have been echoed in countless Jewish homes throughout the ages.

The sixteen women portrayed here are just a small sample of the innumerable Jewish women throughout history who have immersed themselves in lives of Torah and good deeds. Torah was their first love. For these women, there was truly no greater treasure.

S. L.
Jerusalem
Elul 5750/1990